C000092131

Just
Carole

The True Story of Carole Baker

Marianne Hancock

Hochland & Hochland Limited

Published by Hochland & Hochland Limited, 174a Ashley Road, Hale, Cheshire, WA15 9SF, England.

© 1996, Marianne Hancock
First edition

All rights reserved. No part of this book may be reproduced in any form or by any electronic or mechanical means, including information storage and retrieval systems, without permission in writing from the publisher, except by a reviewer who may quote brief passages in a review.

ISBN 1-898507-52-X

British Library Cataloguing in Publication Data
A catalogue record for this book is available from the British Library

Printed in Great Britain by Redwood Books, Trowbridge, Wiltshire

Contents

Acknowledgements

Carole and I would like to thank the following for allowing us to use their real names, genuine locations and factual information: Dr David Silverstein, Consultant Cardiologist of the Nairobi Hospital in Kenya and Dr Khanna, Consultant of Radiotherapy and Oncology, Leicester Royal Infirmary. Also, special thanks to Dr Khanna for his support with writing this book and for giving access to medical notes; the Hodgkin's Disease and Lymphoma Association, PO Box 275, Haddenham, Aylesbury; and last, but by no means least, very special thanks to all Carole's friends and family, most of whose names have remained unchanged - and, in particular, with fondest love and thanks to Carole's mum, sadly no longer with us, dad and Eunice.

A special thanks go to my husband, Pete, and Lynne Inglis.

Prologue

The last thing on my mind was cancer.

Curled up now in the chair, precariously balancing a cup of tea on the arm, I was rather more preoccupied with the thought of what to have for tea.

Flames from the open fire gave a cosy glow to the small, cottage living room. Outside, the January air whistled through the village, occasional footsteps sounding crisp as icy frost blanketed the narrow pavement. It was half past five. Paul would be back home in about an hour. Pinky, my nine year old dog, panted in hot discomfort in front of the roaring logs - determined to roast rather than move. Thumper, the cat, glared at her condescendingly from his majestic repose on the settee, smirking at her scorched foolishness.

I smiled.

Suddenly, my relaxation was interrupted by the phone ringing.

'Hi Carole - it's me, Marianne.'

'Hello!' I was delighted to hear from her. A friend of many years, wading with me at times through the struggles of the past. We gossiped inexhaustibly for several minutes, frivolous, happy chat and newsy updates. Then Marianne hesitated, a pause - and cautiously said,

'Carole, would you like us to write your story?'

I was taken aback, but instantly felt a shiver of excitement run through me.

'Do you think anyone would be interested?' I answered realistically.

'I think you've got something very important to say.'

'What, and tell - it all?'

'It's up to you but I do think the last ten years could make a very special story, an inspirational example of the courage we can all find if we have to. And the book could end with June...' Marianne hesitated, not wishing to tempt fate, 'presuming everything's okay.'

The idea appealed. It was hard to believe that nine years ago I had been diagnosed as suffering from Hodgkin's Disease, a relentless cancer of the lymph system.

My mind slipped back briefly over the past decade - the fear, the fight for survival, the emotional and physical pain, the heartache and sadness... and (with fingers still crossed) the eventual triumph. If telling my story could only help one person, it would be worthwhile.

'What a challenge! You know I'd love to write it - but where on earth would I start?'

'How about from where you left England to go and live in Tanzania?'

Carole Baker
Leicestershire 1991

CHAPTER ONE

Tanzania, 1980

It was March.

Carole's husband, Nick, had recently accepted a transfer through his Leicester engineering firm to work in Dar es Salaam on a non-fixed term contract. He was obsessively interested in bird watching and this move ideally accommodated his love of ornithology.

'Tanzania!' he had enthused, his lean face and blue eyes fired with anticipation, 'just imagine the wild life, the birds…!'

He had travelled there four weeks previously and now Carole, with the children, was leaving England to join him.

Her parents went with them to Heathrow Airport. In the departure lounge, a thread of hurt tied them all in verbal knots, and though they chatted lightheartedly, their voices were strained. Victoria, nine, and Marc, eight, sipped their fruit juices in unusual silence and comradeship, undoubtedly excited at the unfolding adventure stretched out before them but aware too, of heavy hearts. Carole's parents had suffered a few health problems in the last couple of years and, as their only daughter, it both worried and saddened her to be going so far away from them.

Eventually, a voice over the tannoy announced it was time to embark for their flight. After weepy farewells, Victoria, Marc and Carole boarded the plane but, through the tears, uncertainty and family severance, Carole felt a thrill of the unknown stretched invitingly ahead. There was no sense of foreboding, no niggling premonition that anything could possibly go wrong, just a positive, optimistic trust that, at twenty-nine, she had the rest of her happy life - that they all had the rest of their happy lives - lying wonderfully and trouble free in front of them.

Dar es Salaam, the capital, proved to be a beautiful palm fringed town and principal port carved out halfway along the tropical Tanzanian coast. Meaning 'Haven of Peace', the colourful harbour held a mixture of old and new; ancient squat buildings nestled in narrow, winding streets behind broad avenues lined with flame trees, frangipanis and the cascading yellow blossom of the Indian laburnum. Although far from becoming a modern metropolis, original African, oriental and British architecture was now becoming increasingly interwoven with modern hotels and towering administrative office blocks.

It was the latter where Nick now found himself employed, his modern office overlooking the bay where canoes, or ngalawas, meandered amongst cargo ships and fishing boats, bringing in their daily catch to the open air fish market. The children quickly settled down in their new school, easily making new friends, and after a few weeks generally adjusting, they all relaxed contentedly in the informal and colourful atmosphere of Dar es Salaam.

They were a close family, although Nick's bird watching sometimes made Carole and Victoria moan in protest! But he was a good husband and father, a teenage heart-throb who had entered Carole's life at only fifteen. Now, at thirty, his tanned good looks and deep, penetrating eyes could still turn her heart over.

Victoria was the most like her father both in looks and personality. A strong willed, intelligent and strikingly attractive nine year old; lithe, vivacious, with large green inquisitive eyes peering out from under a mop of straight, straw blonde hair. Always talking, always on the go, always wanting to find out how, where, what, if and why. Marc was much more like his mother. Just eleven months younger than Victoria, he was a sensitive, easily upset and gentle child. His features, too, were softer with warm, blond hair tumbling over a freckled face and innocent blue eyes. Perhaps because he could never get a word in edgeways, he had learnt to be aware, observant, intuitive - yet quietly secretive. But he at least followed Nick's love of wild life and shared many bird watching expeditions with him, enjoying a special relationship with his father that Victoria and Carole were excluded from.

Nick's engineering firm had provided them with first class accommodation, a spacious, modern air conditioned bungalow in a rural area called Kurasini, just four bumpy miles from Dar es Salaam. As is the custom there, they were allocated a small domestic staff - a 'house boy', an invaluable live-in local helper able to turn his hand to almost anything, two watchmen on the gates, and a gardener. And, within six months, having made friends with neighbours suffering from surplus pet stock, they acquired two dogs - Kizzy, and a beautiful, sandy coloured puppy, Pinky, in addition to a motley assortment of cats.

Everything seemed ideal. The place, Nick's work, the people, the life, the weather ...none of them had ever felt happier! Nick was finding untiring fulfilment in bird watching, and Carole felt proud that his increasing knowledge and dedication was giving him a respected reputation in ornithology. On one occasion, he actually discovered a previously unknown species of African bird and named it himself. Much of their social life revolved around 'twitchers' (the popular name for bird watchers) and for Nick especially, his growing authority often involved weekends away bird watching, attending meetings or giving lectures.

It was at one such ornithological meeting in January 1982 that Nick met Lynn, a fellow enthusiast. She told him that where she lived in Mufindi, a Brook Bond Tea plantation some 400 miles away, there was a variety of different birds peculiar to that area owing to the elevated, wetter land necessary for growing tea. Nick's immediate enthusiasm had prompted Lynn to invite the four of them to stay with her and her family for a week in April.

So, that Easter, leaving Kizzy, Pinky and the cats under the watchful supervision of their house boy, they ventured the hazardous pot-holed trek through endless scrubland along what is flatteringly called the Tanzam Highway. After about four hours, they entered the Mikumi National Park, a comparatively small 1300 square kilometres of treeless grassland that nevertheless boasted an abundance of wild life - buffalo, zebra, wildebeest, elephant, impala and warthog. They decided to camp over night in the parkland's wooden stop-over cabins which provided very basic accommodation, not very clean, no electricity and no toilet - a crude long drop loo was situated in a shed a few hundred yards away. The most superior amenity being a cold water tap at the back of the cabin.

But any inconvenience was soon forgotten as they watched the animals. Nick and Marc sat motionless with their binoculars, studying grazing buffalo while Victoria teased them relentlessly over the rumoured Mikumi lion allegedly roaming in pursuit of wildebeest, verbalizing occasional sightings and consequently suffering their rude replies! For the most part though, the journey was hot and tedious and it was not until the next day and two punctures later they finally arrived, by then tired and irritable, at their final destination.

Carole had not met Lynn, nor any of her family before, but they welcomed them warmly into their old colonial home. Lynn wore a kanga, the native dress of cotton wrap around, with their youngest two year old daughter carried on her back. She seemed a long, natural inhabitant of rural surroundings and firmly rooted into an African way of life. Smiling broadly, she tossed back her thick brown hair, dark eyes twinkling, revealing premature lines in a weathered complexion. Small, though not particularly slim, she possessed a carefree, unfashionable yet basic attractiveness.

3

Alan appeared by far the more domesticated of the two, and, with the help of their oldest four year old daughter, busily prepared a welcoming pot of tea. He was about fifteen years older than his wife, a tall, good looking man who exercised calm authority, which he was no doubt accustomed to as a high ranking official within the Brook Bond Tea organization.

Within minutes of their arrival, Lynn and Nick were impatiently making plans for mini-expeditions in the local area. Tanzania is renowned for claiming home to literally hundreds of both resident and migratory birds, each with its own particular rarity. Mufindi, as a tea plantation, was then sparsely populated with perhaps only twelve to fifteen families spaciously scattered among the lush expanse of moist fertile land - a haven for the owl and nightjar.

Nick was in his element.

Fuelled with the stimulus of new land, he pored over local maps with Lynn, gloated over photographs and fantasized about the following days while Alan and Carole shared small talk. Like Carole, Alan was vaguely interested but not obsessively so, and as she was content to just relax with the children in new surroundings, she was happy to let them get on with it. Admittedly, after the first couple of days she did feel rather cheated on a one sided holiday. Evenings too left her isolated as they enthusiastically recapped the day, excluding Carole and Alan from their friendship as they shared highlights over chilled glasses of wine before slipping off together in the dark for a last glimpse of the nightjar.

One morning in particular fleetingly puzzled Carole in a different way.

Nick and Lynn had gone down into a wooded area at the bottom of Lynn's garden to set up some nets among the trees, a brief, ten minute procedure to harmlessly snare any species of bird for ringing and observation. However, on this occasion, the pair of them took over thirty minutes and arrived back flushed and dishevelled. It crossed Carole's mind that they were too close for comfort, but Alan remained unperturbed, and as she and Nick were undoubtedly happy together, she dismissed any thoughts as groundless. Anyway, Lynn was not the kind of woman Nick would find physically attractive. Nevertheless, however much Carole tried to be pleased for Nick, who was more vibrant and happy than he'd been for ages, after a week she was struggling to be the happiest of guests and more than ready to make the 400 mile trek home.

They said their goodbyes, thanked them for putting them up and Nick kissed Lynn lightly on the cheek. Carole gave Alan a friendly hug and moved towards Lynn who noticeably recoiled. Carole dismissed the rejection and they left, all waving amicably 'until the next time'.

She was glad to be away.

The journey home was monotonous, weaving through endless miles of flat, uninhabited land interspersed with clusters of primitive thatched huts lying at irregular intervals along the road side.

As they approached the Mikumi National Park yet again, Carole glanced behind her and saw the children were fast asleep. She was reluctant to wake them. Anyway, this provided her with the ideal opportunity to ask Nick about something that was troubling her.

'You and Lynn seemed close,' she risked, 'there isn't anything between you, is there?'

The car radio announced that the Royal Marines had just invaded the Falklands and Nick now seemed intensely riveted to the news. Carole looked at him, waiting for reassurance and noticed his jaw clenching. Suddenly her mouth felt dry. No. Nick liked a pretty woman. He was attracted to femininity and a subtle sophistication - and anyway, physically, they were very close. There was no way Lynn could pose a sexual threat.

Music now played softly on the radio, but still there was an audible slow intake of breath.

'I think I love her.'

Carole felt sick.

The echo of his words seemed to hang suspended in a frozen slice of time. She stared at his hands and noticed his white knuckles gripping the steering wheel, but all she was aware of, all she could hear, were those five words screaming round and round in her head. Then her thoughts started to race frantically in erratic panic to try and normalize everything - remove it, change it, dismiss it. But the swell of nausea in her stomach had registered the blast.

She turned round to check the children were still asleep. Both Victoria and Marc were snoozing soundly, blissfully oblivious to the emotional turmoil in front of them.

The rest of the journey was spent in silence. Carole had a million questions she wanted to hound him with, and yet none. They eventually arrived home with Carole being predominantly angry. Very angry. Very angry with Lynn.

How could she, with her sordid intentions, elbow her way in and intrude into their private relationship? Carole tortured herself, bitterly despising Lynn's evil manipulation. Never did it, nor would she allow it to, enter her mind that Nick was an active participant. Her anger flared into a fight for survival; her and Nick's survival. Although in shock, there were no tears then, just an urgent resolve to save their marriage and destroy this perverse fantasy. How could *he* possibly love *her?*

The sun had already gone down by the time they arrived home at half past six, but although now dark, the children awoke refreshed and hungry. Carole's time was spent preparing them something to eat while Nick unpacked. There was a distance between them; a deliberate, non-communicating space to allow them to function at all, but, if the children suspected any tension, they said nothing.

Later that night, when Victoria and Marc were in bed, and she and Nick were feigning relaxation in the living room, Carole warily broached the subject with him.

'I just don't know what to do,' she sighed, helplessly drained. 'I really just don't know what to do. Perhaps I should write to Lynn.'

'I shouldn't do that,' hastened Nick, and went on to suggest that Carole took a trip to England, attend a wedding in Leicester to which they had both been invited, then stay a couple of weeks visiting family and friends leaving him time to sort out his own feelings.

'No way!' Carole spat emphatically. She was not going to let him out of her sight for even five minutes.

The evening wore on with the unwelcome interruption of local visitors leaving them no time to talk. Finally, they both rolled into bed at midnight. As they lay there together, they were further apart than they had ever been. Carole stared up at the ceiling.

'I still love you, you know,' he whispered softly into the dark.

But she remained silent, feeling wounded in a freshly fractured marriage. Turning on her side, away from her husband, she prayed that sleep might start to fuse the fragments into a kind of healing sense.

When she awoke the next morning, the sun filtered invitingly through the blinds promising a hot, sunny day. She lay there gazing at the dancing particles held in a sunbeam and wondered why her heart ached. Then, with a thundering bolt that slapped her in the face just as it had done the day before, she remembered everything.

Nick stirred uneasily beside her. Carole made a move to slide out of bed when he grabbed her arm.

'I'm sorry.'

Her blood froze. She half wanted to break down and beg him to forget her - and yet felt, too, that she had to apply restraint and control to protect herself. She pulled her arm away and looking coldly at him shrugged her shoulders in resignation as if to imply it was his mess. His fault. He looked so vulnerable and apologetic lying there, his slim, brown body stark naked on the white sheet. Not a man easily prone to emotion or weakness, she so desperately wanted him and needed him then more than ever before.

She turned away.

In the shower, her bruised heart began to demand assertion and gradually a plan began to emerge whereupon she decided to just carry on. She would not ask questions, but try and shelve it on the philosophy that if it's ignored, it will go away. She would tell no-one, not even her closest friends. Finally, she would make an almighty effort to become involved with bird watching.

That day brought the unfolding of a pattern that was to become a familiar routine for several months. A kind of liveable limbo that, considering the circumstances, was the least uncomfortable for all of them.

CHAPTER TWO

Infection After Infection

A month later, Carole and Nick planned a family bird watching expedition to an area some ten miles away called The Saltpans. They arrived on the Saturday and set up camp. Marc and Victoria argued routinely as they helped put up the tent, Victoria bubbling instructions to her protesting brother, while Nick and Carole carefully sorted out valuable photographic equipment. Leaving the children, they then drove to a nearby wooded area to put up some nets before going back to basecamp for a bite to eat. After a light snack, Nick and Carole headed back to the nets but as soon as they got there, they suddenly heard the children screaming. They raced back to the tent and understood from their children's garbled distress that thieves had sneaked in, unobserved, only to be seen as they'd crept away with Nick's expensive camera.

Both Nick and Carole gave chase - just vaguely seeing them in the distance, but sadly, all in vain. All they got from their efforts were badly scratched legs from tearing through the bramble. The day ruined, they packed their bags to return home, furious and heartbroken.

Within a day or two, Carole's legs were sore and swollen. Every scratch from that chase had turned septic. Nick's skin had virtually healed and Carole's reaction appeared unnecessarily dramatic, but however much she tried to bathe and cleanse the cuts, she finally had to have her infected wounds treated medically with both antibiotic cream and a course of penicillin.

Life was not easy.

Carole seemed to be existing on nervous energy, and although, by deliberate design, she and Nick did not discuss his confession from a few weeks previously, the suppression felt like a smouldering volcano threatening eruption.

'Business trips' occasionally took him away for weekends as did so called ornithological meetings and bird watching expeditions, but however suspecting Carole felt, she kept an outward control. An explosion, she knew, could shatter the marriage to pieces. It felt literally held together by restraint.

Carole's own tensions gave way in private, and alone, she would spend many hours crying. She still loved Nick and desperately wanted to keep the family together. She hoped that if they just simply carried on regardless, they might just emerge out of it one day still intact.

However, the stress was beginning to tell and Carole frequently felt extremely tired.

One evening in June, she was preparing their evening meal when she carelessly cut the end of her finger with a chopping knife. Immediately, she rushed to the sink and cleansed the cut thoroughly, letting cold, clear water run over her finger until the bleeding stopped. Then she bathed it in antiseptic before applying a sterile dressing and thought no more about it.

The next day, the end of her finger had swollen like a balloon, the hot, pulsating pressure bulging painfully under the nail. Shocked and concerned, she continued to bathe, disinfect and redress the cut until two days later, the swelling actually prised the nail right off her finger. Carole was horrified! A visit to the doctor meant another course of antibiotics and she had to admit that maybe stress was beginning to affect her general health.

So much so, that when Carole and Nick invited their friends, Heather and her husband, to stay with them one weekend, Carole took a quiet opportunity to pour out all her problems to her friend.

Heather was an intelligent, practical girl with a kind nature and smiling, warm eyes. Her husband worked in Dumilla, a barren outback 150 miles from Dar es Salaam. Amenities were scarce there, and they stayed with Nick and Carole while stocking up on fresh fruit and vegetables in the main town.

On the Saturday afternoon when the two of them were alone, Carole cautiously confessed to Heather that her marriage was in trouble, that Nick loved another woman, that she was trying to carry on as if it wasn't true. As she slowly revealed her unhappiness, layers of tension peeled away in tears. Heather was shocked and upset, responding sympathetically and giving attentive space yet remaining ever practical.

'I just can't believe it of Nick,' she admitted, shaking her head disbelievingly. 'I've always thought of you two as being so ideally suited. It can only be a temporary whim - don't worry. It'll soon blow over.'

And she continued with the comforting assurance that it was surely just infatuation, that Carole was not to let her imagination torture her, that Lynn could not possibly pose any real threat to their marriage. Every couple had ups and downs, every couple had minor flirtations outside the marriage. It was nothing serious. Heather redressed a healthy balance in Carole's thinking, and, coupled with the sheer relief of sharing her problems, after they had gone, Carole was left feeling very much better.

And so, a few days later, Carole decided to tell all to a local neighbour, Tina. Tina had been a very good friend for years, an old Leicester comrade whose husband had a fascination for collecting butterflies and, like Nick, had jumped at the chance of work in Tanzania to further satisfy his interest.

Tina was a small, dynamic brunette, headstrong, dark, with a forthright, direct and open personality. She also owned Cleo, the mother of Carole's dogs - Kizzy and Pinky.

Carole had always valued Tina's friendship. They had a lot in common and often commiserated together over husbands and their obsessions! But it was neither birds, butterflies nor dogs that had prompted her to visit on this particular occasion.

After a couple of hours sheer gossip, Carole hinted at Nick's infidelity. Tina probed further until all was revealed. Her immediate reaction was of absolute disgust; she was appalled and hurled advice with well meaning but destructive concern.

'I should leave him!' she said. 'He doesn't deserve you! How could you put up with that? No, I would get out now.'

Carole felt awful.

She didn't want to hear what her friend was saying. Confused and depressed, Carole sat there while Tina ranted on in dictatorial aggression. All Carole knew was that she didn't want to leave him. She didn't want advice. Just support. But now she felt muddled, useless, weak - and somehow exposed. She would keep quiet in future.

In August 1982, Nick, Carole, Victoria and Marc went back to England for an annual holiday to visit much loved family and friends. Both Nick and Carole had spent their growing years in Enderby, a small village on the outskirts of Leicester, and on their return they usually stayed with Carole's parents who cheerfully endeavoured to house all four of them in their small, cosy, two bedroomed terraced home.

They had a happy two and a half weeks. It was 'winter' back in Dar es Salaam, a dry but cooler season, and they were lucky enough in England to enjoy a fortnight of brilliant sunshine. Lynn seemed a million miles away, and Carole relaxed in the thought their liaison was unavoidably blocked by sheer distance.

It was wonderful seeing everyone again, being with Carole's parents and visiting friends. They all had so much news to catch up on - but Carole didn't say anything about their marital problem. In fact, so far away from Lynn, it felt a brief respite from its existence. Carole had mixed feelings as their holiday ended, wanting to go back home, especially to see her favourite dog, Pinky, again - yet dreading the familiar tension which would inevitably return.

Within a week of being back Carole was ill with food poisoning. She had been vomiting for hours and was doubled up with stomach pains. Eventually she crawled into bed at about five o'clock, spent and drained, longing for Nick's return. She had phoned him earlier at work in a desperate cry for help and he'd promised to come back as soon as he could.

He finally arrived several hours after she'd expected him, and as he breezed by with a glass of water, Carole caught a distinct smell of Lynn's perfume.

The pain in her stomach sank into her heart as she rolled over, letting the tears fall silently and endlessly onto the pillow. If Nick was aware of her crying, he ignored it and left the room as if to give his wife peace and quiet.

The relationship between Nick and Lynn was built purely on the foundations of bird watching. They were both besotted with the obsession of finding rare species of bird and it was this interest that held them together. It posed a challenge that was difficult for Carole to compete with. But sexually, she was on a much better footing.

After thirteen years of marriage, Nick and Carole were still attracted to each other; even throughout the last few months they had somehow maintained a physical relationship. Lynn was not a sensual woman. Maybe Carole would have more success in winning this 'battle' if she exercised even more stimulus and imagination in the field of love.

So, at all times, she made a concerted effort to look seductively at her best. Against her normal, submissive behaviour, Carole grew demanding and frequently took the initiative in lovemaking. Being loving, warm and imaginative, Nick responded with every affection. At least, Carole schemed, he wouldn't be needing sex from her!

Nick was drawing closer to his wife again and began now to regularly want her along on bird watching expeditions. While she was with him, she reckoned, Lynn wasn't - so although, in truth, Carole found the long hours gazing into thin air waiting for a particular bird intensely boring, she determinedly went along with it, even to the extent of neglecting Victoria and Marc. Before, when their father had gone off at the crack of dawn on such an expedition, Carole had stayed at home to cook meals and offer a cosy base of companionship. Now, increasingly, she was gone too, leaving them to fend for themselves.

By October, it was becoming increasingly hot and unbearable. Even two showers a day left everyone unpleasantly clammy, especially when leaving air-conditioned rooms to venture into the blasting furnace of the outside world.

Carole was finding extreme tiredness a problem, too, and although she and Nick were surviving together, there were subtle indications that Lynn still maintained a low but definite profile on the scene.

And she was struggling with this bird watching.

Nick's contribution towards helping their relationship was to try and inspire Carole with an insatiable craving to watch birds. He was prepared to spend long, patient hours teaching her, showing her, advising her. He urged Carole to read, study, research and absorb heaps of knowledge on various species - and finally, gave instructions on how to take good photographs.

But Carole hated it!

It seemed there was only so much they could do for each other without living a total lie. One hot, blistering Sunday Nick and Carole had started arguing during preparations for another bird watching session when Carole was bitten by one of a million midges just hovering around for a succulent sample of blood. Within a few hours, her leg had become severely tender and swollen. The next day it was obvious the bite had flared into an angry infection and, without waiting this time, she visited her doctor for yet another course of antibiotics.

Both her marriage and her health were sliding down again and Carole wondered where on earth it would finally lead to.

Tina, her dominant friend who had long since given up asserting advice on marriage, tried another tactic.

'Why don't you apply for that job vacancy at the British High Commission?' she suggested. 'It will take your mind off things and give you some independence.'

Perhaps she was right.

Carole was struggling now with constant exhaustion which she thought was due to the preoccupying problems always on her mind. She applied for the position and was accepted.

November 1982 and her first job in Dar es Salaam. The work was clerical, based on immigration and passport control and she shared an office with a friendly Lancashire girl called Jean. Jean was slim with long, brown hair, and an attractive young mother of two small children. Very much into alternative health and natural foods, she was married to a teacher at Victoria and Marc's nearby school and they soon became good friends.

Christmas came and went, the hottest time of the year in Tanzania, but although Carole was working harder than ever, she actually felt better than she had for some time.

Then, in January, she scratched her ankle. A small, self inflicted cut as a sharp finger nail accidentally tore the skin.

The following day, her ankle had ballooned into a painfully septic wound. Alarmed at the severe reaction to such a tiny cut, Carole went back to the doctor yet again. This time, he advised her to go to the local hospital and have a bacterial swab taken for analysis. Tests taken on the culture proved inconclusive and it was back to antibiotics once again.

The fourth course in less than a year.

But still it was a New Year - and Carole welcomed the prospect of putting the last one far behind her! She was amazed that, on the whole, she had coped as well as she had.

Or had she?

Maybe a smouldering jealousy and the constant threat of losing Nick was eating away at her health. Couldn't she now even scratch an itch without risking infection? One thing Carole did know was 1982 had been the worst year of her life.

Surely now, things could only get better.

CHAPTER THREE

Just a Little Lump

One Saturday early in March 1983, Muriel, a neighbouring friend, invited Carole to join her with her small daughter, Emma, for an afternoon at Silversands Beach Hotel about twelve miles along the coast. Nick was away attending an ornithological conference while the children were staying with friends and Carole could think of nothing more enjoyable than spending the afternoon with them.

The Tanzanian coastline has just under 500 miles of unspoilt, tropical shoreline with sandy, palm fringed beaches edging the clear Indian Ocean. The Silversands Beach Hotel itself was a rather dilapidated building in need of repair, but it possessed its own quiet stretch of smooth, white sand and blue sea where coral reefs created small lagoons, perfect for safe swimming.

Always good company, Muriel was a cheerful friend with a happy smile and delightful sense of fun, matched only by that of her giggly three year old daughter. She was married to Jim, a doctor of parasitology at the University of Dar es Salaam.

The water was warm and the three of them swam, played and splashed around until they laughingly flopped onto the sand, letting the scorching sun toast their bodies dry. It was one of those precious but increasingly rare times when life felt good. After a few hours, they dusted off the dry sand, dressed themselves and drove over to Carole's home for drinks.

Carole's neck felt tenderly parched and she realized she had burnt her skin. As soon as they got back she went to the bathroom to apply aftersun moisturiser. Gently massaging the cool cream over her shoulders and up her neck, her fingers suddenly felt a small, pea sized, rubbery nodule at the base of her neck, on the left just above the collar bone. She craned to look but it was out of her range of vision so she went over to the mirror. Nothing. No discolouration - except sunburn, not even a small lump visible. But Carole could definitely feel something.

She went into the living room where Muriel and Emma were drinking fruit juice.

'I've got this little lump, Muriel. What do you think it is?' Carole asked, twisting her head and scooping up her long hair for Muriel to look.

'It doesn't really look like anything,' she dismissed after a gentle search. 'I shouldn't worry about it.'

Carole wasn't worried about it, but nevertheless, later that evening after Muriel and Emma had gone home she mentioned it to Nick, volunteering her neck for his examination. He looked and touched but seemed totally unalarmed.

'It's probably nothing,' he shrugged.

His indifference seemed reassuring, although typical of his nature, and she thought little more of it until the following Tuesday when they went to dinner at the home of some local friends, Hilary and Tony.

Both Hilary and her husband were keen on sport and scuba diving and Carole thoroughly enjoyed good food, wine and conversation that wasn't saturated with ornithology. Evenings away from twitchers were good for her and Nick, somehow balancing their differences with the neutral denominator of light hearted conversation and refreshing company.

Also, Hilary was a nurse and after the meal, while Hilary and Carole were making coffee in the kitchen, it seemed an opportune idea to mention the little lump in her neck.

'It's probably just a blocked sweat gland,' Hilary offered, carefully looking and touching Carole's neck with the tips of her fingers, 'but the High Commission where you work have their own doctor visit once a week - why not have a word with her?'

That was a sensible thought, Carole reasoned. The doctor, Dr Sally Son, would be visiting the High Commission the next day to collect X-rays for immigration purposes. Perhaps it might be worth asking her opinion.

The doctor duly arrived and to Carole's surprise showed serious concern over the small nodule. Probing and teasing the little lump between her fingers she questioned her about her general health.

'How do you feel in yourself?' she asked.

'Fine. No problems.' Carole answered, completely forgetting the extreme tiredness and low resistance to infection.

'Hmm. Still, I think you should have a biopsy done. However harmless, it would give you better peace of mind to know it's nothing.'

There were no amenities in Dar es Salaam for having a biopsy but Dr Son persisted with suggestions of travelling back to England for tests.

Suddenly everything seemed blown out of all proportion. Carole felt cross that the little spot couldn't be immediately dismissed - yet common sense led her to exercise some caution. But here was the High Commission doctor firstly suggesting she go to England for a biopsy, then, following Carole's stunned rejection, advising her to go to Nairobi.

'Well,' Carole admitted, 'there is a Company plane where my husband works flying to Nairobi this week.'

'If it's possible, I should go,' she smiled.

Carole phoned Nick to tell him what Dr Sally Son had advised, which he took as an unnecessary palaver, but said he'd make enquiries his end and organize a border permit should it be possible for his wife to travel on that flight.

Nairobi is a beautiful city. Carole had been before under pleasurable circumstances and adored the sunny but cooler climate with its modern skyscrapers, wide roads, nightclubs, cinemas and excellent shops. Only half a century ago, Nairobi had been a town of mud streets and tin houses - but the only natural beauty now still retained was the abundance of tropical flora colourfully lining avenues and precincts. Although a few hundred miles away from Dar es Salaam, it was also the nearest city to possess good medical facilities.

She did not relish the thought of going there at all right then.

It was on Mothers' Day, Sunday 13th March 1983, that Carole boarded the Company plane from Dar es Salaam to Nairobi. Nick took her with her weekend bag of bare essentials to the airport then left her to travel alone. His total lack of concern was both comforting and upsetting. He wasn't at all worried about Carole's general health, which was reassuring but neither did he seem bothered that she was still, nevertheless, going to hospital many miles away on her own. She had at first presumed he would accompany her, but it soon became apparent he considered the event to be a short term nuisance for his wife to sort out by herself.

The plane was a small, twin engined, light aircraft able to seat about eight passengers, but before the flight was ready for take-off, Nick had gone with a casual, cheery wave as if Carole was just going to the local shops. The flight was horrendous.

Sandwiched between a group of engineers and businessmen, she sat petrified while the plane buffeted in violent turbulence through menacing grey storm clouds. As they circumnavigated Mount Kilimanjaro, the aircraft chomped and bashed its way through hailstorms more determinedly than a landrover over the roughest terrain. Miraculously, the pilot landed safely at the expected time of arrival, circling first over the nearby Nairobi National Park where lions prowled only ten minutes drive away from the main city.

Nick had contacted some good friends, Bill and Nancy, who they had met in Libya five years previously. They had never lost touch, and as they now lived in Nairobi, were there to meet Carole off the plane.

Bill was a true Glaswegian, still with a broad Scottish accent and, courtesy of Nick, a fanatical bird watcher. His wife, Nancy, also had Scottish blood in her veins mingled with American. Her flame red hair was in character with a bubbly personality and between them they made a companionable couple.

It was great to see them again. They drove off to their house where Carole was relieved to relax in the rigid stability of a stationary living room, supping tea and exchanging latest news.

Nancy assured Carole it had been arranged she should see a top surgeon at the Nairobi Hospital, Dr David Silverstein, and that this had been especially engineered through a direct contact of Lynn's. Obviously, neither Bill nor Nancy knew of any marital problem and they purely related this news as they had heard it via Nick. Just hearing the name 'Lynn' knotted Carole's stomach.

The following Tuesday, Bill and Nancy volunteered to take Carole to the huge, modern hospital and insisted on staying themselves before taking her back to their place after her afternoon appointment. Buzzing with activity, the hospital maintained an air of prompt efficiency and within a short time Carole was having a private consultation with Dr Silverstein.

For all his high, respected authority, he was a kind man with a smilingly lined face framed with distinguished greying hair. He offered tender concern, slowly allowing ample time to explore her health.

Did she tire easily? Feel run down? Had she suffered loss of appetite or night sweats? Was she losing weight or having any pains?

Carole answered him honestly that she did become tired easily - but that she also led a hectic life.

Lying on the examination couch, he thoroughly probed her neck, gently feeling too around her groin and liver. Then she had some chest X-rays taken followed by blood tests before going to a reception area to await the results.

Carole felt quite relaxed, sure now that everything was going to be resolved, and idly flicked through the pages of some magazine digesting none of its contents and just wishing to go back home. After a short while, a pretty nurse called her back into Dr Silverstein's consulting room where he warmly beckoned her to take a seat opposite his huge leather chair and paper stacked table.

'Now, can you come into hospital this evening?' he asked, 'then we can take a piece of tissue from this small lump of yours first thing in the morning and keep you in for a couple of days just to check everything out.'

A cold wave of anxiety washed over her.

She knew she had come to Nairobi for a biopsy, but had somehow imagined a thorough examination would make it unnecessary. The consultant's nurse went on gently to explain it would be a straightforward procedure with minimum discomfort.

Carole felt dazed as she wandered off to find Bill and Nancy. Everything seemed so unreal it was difficult to believe what was happening. A little over a week ago, there had been no lump to her knowledge. Her life, unhappy as it had been, had at least held some semblance of order.

Now it felt a mess. Uncertain, chaotic and so unreal. There she was in Nairobi, a large, unfamiliar town, unbelievably planning a short stay in a totally strange hospital hundreds of miles from home. She felt so isolated and detached - even from herself.

Ever helpful and supportive, Bill and Nancy assured Carole they could just go straight back, collect her sparse belongings and return immediately. Within a couple of hours Carole was back at the Nairobi Hospital again, now in a small private room as an inpatient with nothing to eat or drink allowed. And as the nurses flitted in and out, the evening brought increased fear and loneliness.

Carole was woken at half past five the next morning, Wednesday 16th March, by two nurses jollying her along to have a shower. Standing there under the refreshing spray of water, her throat was dry and her stomach churned with apprehension. After she was clean and dry, she dressed herself in the statutory white gown and went back to her hospital bed for the pre-med. Carole knew her biopsy was scheduled for eight o'clock, but after a tranquillizing injection, could remember no more until after midday.

The first thing she recalled as she hazily swam in and out of consciousness was a nurse taking blood out of her arm. Although only half awake, she thought it strange now it was over to still be subjected to tests.

As the day wore on, Carole gradually regained awareness and by the evening was delighted to have Bill and Nancy visit. A familiar philosophy had taken over as self-protection; ignore it and it'll go away. Just as when she had learnt of Nick's affection for Lynn, she now employed the same strategy of asking no questions. That way, she would learn of nothing to worry about.

Carole knew it was sheer avoidance, but it helped her and she deliberately displayed a bright, unconcerned manner towards the nurses, and Bill and Nancy. Her recovery from the anaesthetic was quick, and she was soon able to have a bite to eat and enjoy cheerful company.

On the Thursday, Carole received some beautiful flowers and cards from well wishing friends, but she still hadn't heard from Nick. Maybe he'd phoned Bill and learnt she was fine from him. The nurses were very kind and friendly and chatted with Carole in light hearted fun. She was much more relaxed now the biopsy was behind her and was told she should be able to leave hospital the next day, as soon as all the results were completed.

At eight o'clock on Friday morning, Dr Silverstein came into Carole's room with a nurse and sat on the edge of her bed.

'We've run some tests on the biopsy,' he said slowly, 'and you've got an illness called Hodgkin's Disease.'

'Oh, it's got a name...?' Carole answered naively.

'Yes. Now, this illness is curable - but not in Nairobi.'

'Do I have to go back to England, then?'

'I do advise it,' he urged gently, and he placed his hand on hers, patting it as if in confirmation.

CHAPTER FOUR

A Short Course of Treatment

Quietly they went away, leaving Carole with a meaningless diagnosis which she accepted without question. She didn't ask what Hodgkin's Disease was, what the treatment might be or how long she would have it for. That way, she could organize her own diagnosis and stay in control.

There was no fear, no anxiety - just a calm, preoccupied awareness that she had some temporary health problem. In fact, Carole was almost pleased. Now she would go to England and receive treatment, probably a special course of antibiotics. Of course! It was just a blocked sweat gland as Hilary had suggested, maybe with some bacterial infection. Nick would feel concerned and care for his wife, give her lots of love and attention. Perhaps they could all travel over for her week or two of medication - a bonus holiday! Then everything would be fine. They would come back to Dar es Salaam and Nick would never want to see Lynn again.

With all that sorted out in her mind, Carole asked a nurse if she could telephone her husband.

'Of course,' she smiled sympathetically, patting Carole's arm. 'Try not to worry.' Appreciating her kindness, but not at all worried, Carole dressed herself ready to leave, packed her weekend bag and went to the reception area to phone Nick.

'I have something called Hodgkin's Disease,' she told him, 'and I have to go to England for a week or two for treatment - but it's quite curable,' Carole continued optimistically, 'it's just that they can't do it here.'

After Carole had explained her version of the story, it was arranged he would book her a flight direct from Nairobi to Heathrow. Nick and the children would fly from Dar es Salaam and they would all meet together at Heathrow Airport, as closely timed together as possible.

Then Carole rang Nancy and Bill who said they'd be there to pick her up shortly. Just sixty minutes later, they drove up to the main entrance of the hospital. Happy to see them, Carole eagerly walked towards the car carrying her weekend bag and climbed into the back seat. But Nancy's eyes were red and swollen as if she had been crying and through her smiles Carole sensed she was unhappy. Feeling an intrusion into what was obviously a private argument, she immediately obeyed Nancy's persuasion to go and lie down as soon as they reached their home.

'You must rest,' she insisted, 'anaesthetic weakens the body and you need to build up your strength as much as you can.'

As Carole lay on the bed gazing up at the ceiling, a thought flashed through her mind that Nancy's tears might have been for her. Then she remembered the nurse's over sympathetic smile when she'd asked to phone Nick. Try not to worry, the nurse had said. Could she be really ill?

Hurriedly, Carole shrugged the negative thoughts to the back of her mind and dreamed of going to England. She loved seeing mum and dad, family, old friends, the little village... but as she drifted off into a troubled sleep, her heart ached for her favourite dog, Pinky. How she would have loved to nestle in the soft, golden fur, nuzzle her neck, caress her ears and savour the warmth.

Back in Dar es Salaam, Nick had been in touch with Jim, Muriel's husband. Jim was a doctor of parasitology and Nick asked him if, in his medical capacity, he knew anything about Hodgkin's Disease.

Not realizing the question was related to his wife, Jim answered without choosing his words too carefully, explaining that it was a rare, often relentless cancer of the lymph glands spreading quickly from one group of nodes to another until it eventually invaded the blood and liver. Treatment by radiotherapy, chemotherapy or both, depended on the progressive stage of the cancer but it had to be a race against time to prolong life for more than a year or two.

That was 1983 and Hodgkin's Disease was then only just beginning to claim some modest success with treatment if caught early enough.

Nick had been devastated.

He'd immediately phoned Bill and Nancy, pouring out the seriousness of Carole's illness to them in floods of tears. Then, somehow, he had driven to the children's school, collected Victoria and Marc and broken the tragic news to them.

Of course, Carole was blissfully ignorant of all this, still believing it to be some straightforward bacterial infection. There was, she knew, an underlying tension in the drama because it was so intense and fast moving;

but she was becoming adept at side-stepping anxiety and anyway, England was good news because it kept Nick and Lynn apart.

Carole was aching to see Nick and the children again. Fortunately one of Nick's bosses from the Nairobi branch of the company called by with an air ticket for her to fly to Heathrow the next evening, and a phone call from Nick that night confirmed his flight with Marc and Victoria was due to touch down in London just three hours after his wife's arrival. Nick's brother, Gary, and his wife, Eunice, would be there to meet them in their car. Also, John, Carole's brother-in-law, was in his, to transport them all back to Leicester.

Carole asked Nick to pack any warm clothes he thought she might need. March in England was likely to be cold, and Carole had only a few very inappropriate summer dresses with her in Nairobi. He was so warm and tender on the phone, his voice loaded with emotion, telling Carole how much he loved her, that she wasn't to worry about anything and how he couldn't wait to hold her closely in his arms again.

If this is what had to happen to win him back again, it would be worth it.

Bill and Nancy took Carole, still with only her weekend bag, to Nairobi Airport for the flight to Heathrow due to depart at just past midnight on Saturday 19th March. She also had some biopsy samples clinically sealed in a wooden casket and two X-rays which Dr David Silverstein had instructed her to take to her own doctor in Leicester, causing chaos with officials as Carole explained her need to pass through customs security without infra-red scanning.

Bill and Nancy both had tears in their eyes as they hugged her goodbye. They had been wonderful and couldn't have shown more genuine concern. Of course, they knew more than Carole did, and as they embraced her, they must have wondered if they would ever see their friend again.

'Do take care!' they chorused. 'We'll write soon - and don't forget, keep taking the pills!'

With a final wave, Carole boarded the plane and resigned herself to the long, tedious journey back to England, which at least would soon bring her close to her family again.

She landed at Heathrow at quarter past six on a bitterly cold Sunday morning, ridiculously clad in a scanty summer dress much to the amazed stares from other passengers. Shivering violently, Carole's eyes searched for a familiar face. Suddenly, she spotted Eunice waving both arms frantically in a bid to attract her attention. Oh, lovely Eunice! Soon, they were all together and they headed towards the airport lounge for a longed for cup of tea.

Eunice had always been a wonderful friend, blonde, pretty, softly spoken and sincere, a nurse, and never before had Carole been so pleased to see her. She was a deeply caring person, and as her velvety brown eyes smiled warmly into hers, Carole suddenly felt like crying. But she didn't, and they all chatted lightheartedly about nothing too important, skating over health problems as a mere inconvenience. Fortunately, they'd had the foresight to bring a thick, chunky sweater and Carole huddled now into it's welcoming warmth.

Gary, Eunice's husband and Nick's younger brother, brought a tray of hot drinks. He was very like Nick, good-looking, rugged, slim. As they chatted together, Carole felt so grateful for their presence. They must have been as tired as her having driven down to London through the night from the Midlands.

Nick's plane landed at nine o'clock in the morning and they hovered in anticipation around the Arrival Terminal.

Carole felt drained.

Her energy level was low anyway because of her health, but the stress and strain of the last couple of weeks, combined with the long flight, washed over her in weary weepiness. It was all she could do to hold onto her emotions - until she saw Nick, Victoria and Marc.

As Carole suddenly spotted them, she ran towards them and lunged desperately into Nick's arms, breaking down and weeping uncontrollably. Nick held her close and she could feel the dampness from his own tears as they clung together. Oblivious to the crowds of travellers swarming around, they swept Victoria and Marc into the reunion.

A small light shone through Carole's tears. They were all together. Everything would be all right. She had Nick back again. She just needed to get rid of this silly infection and life would be just as it had been once before.

CHAPTER FIVE

Cancer

The children were travelling to Leicester with Gary and Eunice. John had volunteered to take Nick and Carole in his car, and they sat in the back, Nick's arm protectively around his wife.

'Don't worry,' Nick assured Carole caringly, 'we'll fight this cancer between us.'

Cancer? What did Nick mean, cancer? She didn't have cancer.

Did she?

'Cancer?' Carole asked blankly. 'I don't have cancer, do I?'

Nick froze in his seat. She could sense his rigid tension right there next to her. A strangled silence held them all in their own panic, none of them daring to hardly breathe or move.

'*Nick!* Carole suddenly screamed, shattering the ice with an explosive blast, '*I don't have cancer do I?*'

'I'm sorry,' he whispered limply, 'I had no idea you didn't know.'

So that was it.

Hodgkin's Disease was cancer.

Oh no. Oh God no. She'd been here before. Her stomach felt like it did almost a year ago; heaving, nauseous, sick.

Cold panic washed over her in chilling waves. She couldn't take it. Not this. First Lynn - and now cancer. Fool! Fool! Fool! Why did she always bury her head in the sand only to eventually and unavoidably have the brutal, stark truth slapped in her face? Oh, dear God. Wilting quickly in despair, Carole clutched at Dr Silverstein's easy words.

'It's curable… Dr Silverstein said it was quite curable…'

'Yes, yes,' confirmed Nick, no wiser than Carole on this score.

'Cancer of what?' she asked eventually.

'Of the lymph system, I think. That's why you found a lump in your gland, but I really don't know much.'

'Does everyone else know?'

Suddenly she remembered Nancy's emotional farewell, Marc and Victoria's urgent hugs at the airport - and what about Eunice, Gary and John? And her parents? Nick's parents? Did they all know?

'They all know you've got Hodgkin's Disease. Whether they realize it's cancer I don't know. But does it matter what it is? You've come back to have treatment and get well again.' Nick's arm tightened around his wife and he kissed her hair.

'You will look after me, won't you?'

'Yes, I promise.'

Through the shock and dark, foreboding pathway now suddenly ahead, Nick's promise held a thread of compromise. The price was heavy, but right then, they felt closer together than they had in ages.

At Carole's parents' house, her mum looked drawn with desperate anxiety in her eyes. She had rarely seen her mother without a smile. She was always laughing, a comfortable, cuddly and loveable mum, gentle, caring and easy going.

'What on earth is going on?' she now cried, bewildered.

Carole felt remote.

Upstairs in the spare bedroom she could hear Victoria and Marc unpacking.

'Yes, it is cancer,' Nick was explaining, 'but it is curable.'

'Seven years it took us to get her. We're not going to lose her now.'

Did they know she was there? Was she dreaming? She was in the room with them, but they were talking about her, not to her. Perhaps it wasn't real. Carole felt so strange, so unbelievably detached, a foreigner encompassed in her own childhood home of memories. 'Seven years to get her. We're not going to lose her now.' The words penetrated her senses with a befuddled threat of death. Yes, it had taken seven years for Carole's parents to conceive their one and only child - but lose her now?

Could she die? What the hell was this thing called Hodgkin's Disease?

Carole had an appointment with the family practitioner for nine o'clock the next morning, the first day of spring - March 21st. Nick went with her armed with X-ray and biopsy.

'Sit down,' the doctor nodded at the two seats opposite his busily cluttered oak desk.

'Carole's got Hodgkin's Disease and we need to see a consultant immediately,' insisted Nick.

The doctor raised his eyebrows bemusedly and, tilting back in his chair, smiled in calm disbelief.

'Oh yes? Now, how do you know that?'

Nick explained the whole saga of the previous month whilst Carole sat there, distanced, abandoned and totally malleable until they finally left with an appointment for her to see Dr Wilkinson, a haematologist at the Leicester Royal Infirmary, the next day.

Dr Wilkinson examined Carole thoroughly, probing as Dr Silverstein had, all round her neck, armpits, groin and liver. A blood test was taken and notes on her general health accounted for until he felt confident in confirming the diagnosis. Only he found two more lumps - one in the other side of her neck and one under the armpit.

An appointment was made for Carole to have a bone marrow extraction the following day, an unpleasant sounding procedure but as it was only as an out-patient for a couple of hours, she thought it must be fairly straightforward.

Letters had begun to arrive at her parents' house in Enderby. Kind, warm promises of barbecues on the beach and celebratory dinner parties on her return. Carole opened one addressed to both her and Nick and quivered in rage. 'Anything I can do...' it read. Carole's eyes cast coldly down to the scrawled signature - 'love Lynn and Alan.' With bitter deliberation, she tore the letter to shreds.

'Don't be like that,' Nick muttered, 'she's only trying to help.'

Help, Carole thought ironically. She's caused the bloody cancer.

The Leicester Royal Infirmary offered a meandering maze of old, narrow corridors with ageing signs to various destinations. Eventually, they found the small, six-bedded examination ward for Carole's bone marrow extraction and she was instructed by a young nurse to slip behind some screens and curl up into a fetal position on the bed. The nurse offered her small hand.

'If it hurts, squeeze it,' she smiled.

Carole had not been permitted any general anaesthetic as it would have been detrimental to the test, and although she was given a local anaesthetic, it was impossible to actually freeze the bone. The doctor explained the test was to check there were no cancerous cells in the marrow which could indicate leukaemia, and although it was expected to prove clear it was necessary to definitely rule it out.

He held a large, hollow needle and punched it deeply through the pelvic bone. Instantly, Carole was consumed with scolding pain and crunched the poor nurse's hand in agony. There was an excruciating suction sensation as the doctor withdrew some brown marrow and Carole managed to think how weird it was to look at the vacuumed contents of her own body. A stranger to her own inner self, he had found a hidden part of her that looked like congealed dog meat - but it was still a bit of her! The doctor placed the extracted samples onto a dozen slides and then plunged the needle in once more, spreading the soft, brown second helping into a bottle of clear solution.

Carole and Nick then travelled home on the bus - a bouncing, rough forty minute ride of unadulterated torture. Violently bruised, she wailed silently all the way back.

On March 30th it was Carole's birthday. She was thirty-one and although they tried to celebrate, she felt daunted at the prospect of further hospital tests before the start of whatever brief treatment might be deemed necessary. They were all impatient to return home to Dar es Salaam. Already things were becoming more time consuming and complicated than Carole had imagined, but an appointment with Dr Khanna at the Leicester Royal Infirmary the next day would probably move things along.

Nick went with her. Dr Khanna was a dark, austere man with a quiet, professional authority that was both reassuring and awe-inspiring. His black eyes expressed forthright honesty but lacked sympathetic compassion. Carole decided she wouldn't like to waste his time. After a thorough examination and routine questioning, he invited her to sit with Nick while he explained a few things. First of all, the bone marrow had proved clear.

Secondly, in the past all Hodgkin's Disease sufferers had automatically had their spleen removed as a matter of course. This had necessitated a patient remaining on drugs for life but the operation was now being considered unnecessary in the light of modern, improved, treatment.

Carole felt cautious, as if he was offering the good news before the bad, and he completed the deal with three more dates for exhaustive tests and X-rays.

On April 7th Carole was to have a body scan, on April 13th a liver scan and on April 14th a complicated sounding procedure called a lymphangiogram. Confused, disappointed and irritated, she reluctantly resigned herself to the fact it would still be a few weeks before she could resume normal living again. The medical profession had labelled her illness and she felt fine in herself. Why couldn't she just take the pills and go home?

Nick and Carole had been enjoying meeting up with friends in Leicester and were managing quite an active social life. Carole's parents were being really kind and supportive, encouraging them to go out whenever they wanted and willingly offering to keep an eye on Victoria and Marc. She and Nick were getting on well together and it almost felt as if Lynn was a dark memory from the past.

One day, an old bird watching friend called Mike phoned up and told Nick and Carole that he had a cousin, Mary, who'd been treated for Hodgkin's Disease the year before. Would they like to meet her? Mike went on to explain that he and his wife, Paula, were visiting his parents on Sunday for tea with Mary and he knew they would be more than welcome to join them.

Mary was about 28; she looked well and was back to leading a full life. Carole tried to chat with her about Hodgkin's Disease and her treatment but she seemed non-committal. Carole guessed it all seemed in the past to her now, and anyway, there was little real comparison. Mary's cancer had obviously been much more advanced than hers, having involved chemotherapy which she appeared reluctant to talk about, but she wore a wig so Carole knew she had lost her hair. However, because of the disparity between their respective illnesses, there seemed no relevant link although Carole did admire how brave she had been and was delighted to have met her.

On April 7th, Carole arrived at the Leicester Royal Infirmary for her body scan, then a revolutionary new method of taking X-rays, and the first of her three exploratory tests.

First of all, she was asked to drink a litre of unpleasant, aniseed flavoured liquid. Struggling and shuddering with every mouthful - as much from anxiety as from the distasteful contents - she finally managed to get it all down while a patient nurse explained how the liquid would clearly show under the scan if there were any undiscovered areas of concern. The scan itself was absolutely painless and just involved Carole lying on the X-ray couch for thirty minutes whilst modern technology clicked away. The results would be sent to Dr Khanna alongside the results from her following two tests and a final course of treatment would then be assessed on the collective information.

At least some kind of end was in sight, and no-one could say they weren't being fast, efficient and thorough.

On April 13th, Carole went for a liver scan. Following an injection of isotope into her arm vein, she had a scan taken twenty minutes later by a square X-ray machine strategically placed over her liver. It was a painless procedure which took about half an hour after which she was allowed to go home. Again it was explained that the isotope used in the test would show up any irregularity in the liver and that the result would be sent straight to Dr Khanna.

The next day, she had an appointment for a lymphangiogram, an X-ray of the lymph vessels and nodes and the test was in two parts, spread over two days.

First of all, she had a small needle inserted between the first and second toe of each foot which slowly injected a greeny-blue dye into the fine lymph vessels. After about ten minutes, the dye had been drawn up, clearly exposing the lymph vessels over the top of her feet. Then, a local anaesthetic was administered to 'freeze' the skin followed by a small slit in each foot to accommodate the insertion of fine needles into the actual lymph vessels. A radio-opaque dye was then slowly pumped under slight pressure to gradually fill the vessels from the feet, up the legs and into the abdomen.

It was tedious and uncomfortable. Carole had to lie perfectly still for three hours on a hard X-ray couch and she felt slightly unwell. Eventually, a mobile X-ray machine was manoeuvred over her to take sliced, segmented shots of her lower half; part two to be continued the next day. The needles were removed and a dressing put on. At least she would not have to have them inserted for the latter part of the procedure as the already injected dye would continue to travel slowly upwards. The next day's continued lymphangiogram was therefore done without needles and in less than half the time.

Now all she had to do was await Dr Khanna's final verdict.

CHAPTER SIX

Radiotherapy

Monday 18th April was a warm spring day. Daffodils bloomed, birds sang, Nick and Carole were fine and Carole felt well. Ridiculously well, in fact. It seemed a farce to be visiting Dr Khanna to discuss treatment for a disease she couldn't relate with or attach herself to. She couldn't see it - except for one, tiny palpable nodule (Carole had never been able to find any others), and she just did not feel ill. She was no longer tired, run down or sad, nor had she suffered any further infected cuts or scratches. It was almost as if she was now somehow cured and she half expected Dr Khanna to dismiss any treatment as unnecessary.

Nick accompanied his wife, both of them beaming optimistically, literally full of the joys of spring as they entered Dr Khanna's consulting room.

Dr Khanna smiled. He was pleased with the results. There was no trace of Hodgkin's Disease anywhere else, just the neck and under the left arm. A short course of X-ray treatment should resolve the problem and he suggested Carole undergo seventeen doses of deep X-ray therapy over approximately a three week period.

Although she was disappointed to have to endure any treatment at all, it didn't register as radiotherapy and his wording offered it as an acceptable solution.

'I'll be able to go to Tanzania in the summer, then?'

'If all goes well,' Dr Khanna nodded.

Thank goodness, she sighed silently. Carole yearned now to go back. She longed for them all to be a close family again in Dar es Salaam - for there would be no Lynn to worry about now. That was finished. It would be just the four of them, and the animals.

Oh, Pinky! Carole couldn't wait to see Pinky! Her thoughts wandered away, and she was there... she would decorate the living room, recover the settee, take Pinky and Kizzy long, lazy strolls; she would cook cosy, intimate meals; she would...

'...for lung plates,' Dr Khanna added.

Carole hadn't been listening to a word!

Snatched back to reality, she gazed at him, trying to piece together anything she should have been hearing.

Lung plates? What for?

Nick was nodding with intent concentration. Slowly, Carole began to grasp that she would need to be measured up for lung protection plates before deep X-ray therapy, that she needed indelible blue marker dots tattooed on her chest to accurately line up protection plates before treatment. What a performance, she thought. However, Carole was duly measured up and 'tattooed' and told she would receive a phone call within the next few days telling her when to come in for the first session.

On the way back to Carole's parents' house, Nick put his arm around her reassuringly.

'You know I'm going to have to go back to work, don't you?' he said.

She did know.

And the children would have to go back to school, but she had put off admitting it because she didn't want them to go. In her mind, there was this fixed picture of them all going back together.

'I shall be able to come with you if you can just wait another three weeks,' Carole persuaded. But she knew really they had already stayed a month and each of them had commitments back home to carry on with.

'I'll stay another week,' Nick promised. 'Then I'll have to go back - but it won't be long before you can join us.'

He would stay for their fourteenth wedding anniversary on Tuesday 26th April, and they planned a romantic meal for that night. Even the thought of being separated from them all for a few weeks while she had her radiotherapy still couldn't detract from an optimistic sense of hope on the horizon. At least it would all soon be over. It wouldn't be long now before everything was back to normal. Better than normal! Nick and Carole were getting on really well and she felt all her troubles would soon be over.

Unfortunately, the planned romantic meal was not to be as Carole received a phone call to say her course of radiotherapy treatment was due to start on 26th April - their wedding anniversary. Celebrations would have to be carried out in the leadened bowels of the Leicester Royal Infirmary.

31

Carole felt apprehensive that morning but not scared. She had endured enough X-rays in the course of diagnosis to remove the fear of the unknown and she only saw the treatment as a course of further X-rays. Nick went with her and they both laughed as they approached what had been humourously labelled 'The Mega-Volt Suite'. A nurse asked Carole her name and told her to go into a cubicle, pick up a blue and white checked gown and go back to the waiting room. There were about five patients already there and Carole felt conspicuously young.

After a while, a nurse beckoned Carole to follow her down a small corridor into an end room which looked like something out of a sci-fi film. An enormous, complex machine dominated the area with a complicated table displaying an array of controls, while around the walls television monitors focused in on a central maze of equipment. Two nurses cheerily explained that Carole was to lie on the 'table' for only one minute and that the machine would give thirty seconds of therapy on her front, then swivel automatically to repeat treatment on her back. Carole took off her gown, climbed onto the table and had the lung plates placed over her. The two blue tattoos were strategically lined up with overhead pin point lights and she was asked to keep quite still, but breathe normally.

The nurses then hurried away to observe her through the television screens, leaving Carole alone in the menacing hum of machinery. Carole counted each and every one of those sixty seconds in paralysed suspense.

'You might feel a bit sore,' one of the nurses advised her afterwards, 'and maybe notice a slight reddening of the skin - but just dust the area with baby powder. Don't use soap or deodorant.'

No problem.

She was relieved. Just a minute of painless therapy and that was all there was to it.

Later that day, Carole's skin was warmly glowing and she felt tired. She went to bed and fell asleep for the afternoon. The next two days were the same. The radiotherapy itself was no problem but always a couple of hours later, there was an immense tiredness and an increasingly uncomfortable burning glow.

On Friday, there was no treatment. And Nick and the children were due to fly back to Tanzania.

With heavy heart, Carole helped Nick and Gary to load the car for the journey down to Heathrow Airport. Gary's wife, Eunice, joined them too, and although it was rather a squeeze with six of them plus all the baggage in Gary's car, Carole was glad to have Eunice there.

In the Departure Lounge, the impending wrench was tearing Carole to shreds. She clung on tearfully to Nick and when it was time for him and the children to board their flight, they held each other like limpets. Once they'd gone, Carole felt totally bereft, abandoned and broken hearted.

She knew now that she had to fight alone - and quickly. Her burning urgency was to be back with them. She felt desperate to get there, ready to fight tooth and nail through every obstacle until she, too, could go home.

As the radiotherapy continued, her health weakened. The skin around her neck grew increasingly tender, the tiredness was constant, her appetite poor and she was beginning to feel permanently nauseous.

Perhaps it was unwise to have accepted a dinner invitation at Mike and Paula's, the relatives of Mary who'd had Hodgkin's Disease. In their ignorance they had prepared a hot curry and although Carole struggled painfully with a few mouthfuls, the burning spices scorched her already burnt throat and she soon apologetically had to admit defeat.

Then, halfway through the treatment, Carole showered one morning and was blow-drying her long hair when she noticed a chunk of hair on the brush. Horror washed over her as she deliberately swept the brush up the back of her head repeatedly; the hair at the back was just coming away in brushes full. Carole rushed to the mirror, twisting and contorting herself to see the damage. A deformed plate sized circle of bare, white scalp glared from the base of her neck to the crown.

She combed her hair down frantically trying to make it disappear, then swept it up again and just stared, mortified, at her reflection. Panic washed over her as she hopelessly tried to think what she could do. Carole looked at the brush. Half a head of long, dark hair dangled lifelessly from the bristles. She sat down and cried.

She had just lost half her hair.

The radiotherapy treatment now seemed to be dragging on. Three weeks turned into five owing to a Bank Holiday and other interruptions. Carole's original relief over the treatment had turned into dread. She felt sick, weary and sore.

Happily, Nick phoned to tell his wife that he had managed to organize a UK business trip and would be able to stay in Leicester for five days in the last week of May. This dove-tailed perfectly with the end of Carole's radiotherapy treatment, enabling Nick to go with her for a conclusive appointment with Dr Khanna on May 30th.

33

She had had another body scan to hopefully confirm the success of the therapy and the results of this would be given to Dr Khanna before her appointment. There were no longer any detectable lumps and, apart from the side effects of the treatment, she felt sure she would now be allowed to go home.

It was good seeing Nick again and Carole even wondered if she might be able to go back with him in five days time. Mentally, she started packing her bags, unable to quell a euphoric anticipation of the big 'All Clear'.

Dr Khanna smiled and invited Nick and Carole to sit down. He talked briefly to Nick about Africa as Carole wriggled impatiently. Eventually, he turned to look at his patient, his dark eyes now expressing serious concern.

'Now,' he said, 'the radiologists have found slight irregularities in the lymph system. I don't personally think there are, but they do.'

What was he saying? With bated breath, Carole listened in wary confusion.

'To be on the safe side,' Dr Khanna continued, 'as you will eventually be going back to Tanzania where I won't be able to keep an eye on you, I would like you to start a course of chemotherapy.'

What did that mean?

That she couldn't go home?

Suddenly it hit her and she burst into tears.

And chemotherapy?

Never had she felt so tormented in her life before. Her conjured up knowledge of such horrendous treatment filled her with despair.

'Doesn't that make you sick?' was all she could whimper through her tears.

'Some patients are sick, some aren't. Often, it's in the mind.'

Somewhere in the distance, Carole could hear him talking about six monthly treatments, two parts to each one - that was twelve sessions of chemotherapy - but she was beyond hearing anything.

CHAPTER SEVEN

Chemotherapy

Nick was sympathetic and supportive, yet somehow Carole sensed a slight distance between them again. She was engulfed with self-pity, and couldn't have been a very cheerful and loving wife to have around anymore, and although he promised to be with her for her first session of chemotherapy, due to be administered in just four days time, Carole felt he didn't really want to stay.

Maybe he, too, dreaded her chemotherapy and having been back to Dar es Salaam and his familiar routine, albeit without his wife, now felt impatient to return.

For Part A of Chemotherapy 1, the first therapy, Carole was asked to stay overnight for observation although on subsequent sessions she would be able to leave after treatment.

At nine o'clock on Friday morning 3rd June 1983, Carole duly arrived at the Leicester Royal Infirmary with Nick. He accompanied her to St Mary's Ward where she was led into a side annex and given a blood test. Nick then left, telling her he'd be back later that afternoon.

Carole was terrified.

Although in future she would find St Mary's Ward active with chemotherapy patients on Fridays, that day there was only one other 'first-timer', a poor Asian woman who could not speak English.

The blood test proved satisfactory and a nurse told Carole to slip into her nightdress, move into the main ward and lie on a bed. With her heart racing at break neck speed, she tried to read but her mind whizzed with dread. What would it be like? Would she be sick? When would it happen? What would happen? How would she feel?

Eventually, lunch time came and dinner was served - fish with salad. Somehow, that felt reassuring. Surely they wouldn't serve dinner if they expected her to be sick? After all, Dr Khanna had said some patients weren't ill and that often, anyway, it was just in the mind. Perhaps her kind of chemotherapy wouldn't have any adverse side effects.

Carole was surprisingly hungry and ate it all.

At three o'clock Dr Khanna came onto the ward and shortly arrived at the foot of Carole's bed. After asking how she felt, he proceeded to explain they were now going to administer the treatment. A nurse attached a saline drip solution to her and she asked what drugs would be involved. Although Carole later learned that her chemotherapy was a combination called 'MOPP' (nitrogen mustard, oncovin, prednisone and procarbazine), she was told at the time that it consisted of mustard gas, Madagascan Periwinkle plant and an antisickness drug.

She was relieved at the latter, thinking that that should remove any threat of nausea. However, the first two drugs made Carole smile nervously as they sounded more like herbal ingredients from an alternative health source, and the Madagascan Periwinkle was a rampant weed-like flower which spread rapidly in her own garden in Dar es Salaam!

Another nurse joined them carrying a tray with syringes.

'We're just going to inject these substances into the saline solution,' explained Dr Khanna, 'and these will then flow intravenously into your body for a few minutes before we take them all away.'

That sounded harmless enough.

After ten minutes, a nurse came and removed all the equipment then put a small sticking plaster on her arm.

'You might as well lie down and read now,' she suggested kindly.

Carole was okay! It was over! She felt fine - no nausea, no nothing! Just enormous relief that she had now completed her first session of chemotherapy. Dr Khanna had gone and just the nurses breezed around unhurriedly in a calm air of reassurance. Also, Carole noticed there was no sick bowl which confirmed her assumption she was not likely to vomit. She tried to read her book, and slowly, all the past anxiety dissolved as she started to relax.

At half past four that afternoon a cold, queasy wave of nausea briefly washed over her. She told herself strictly that it was in her mind and buried her nose more deeply into the book. Ten minutes later, she suddenly sat bolt upright knowing she was about to be sick. Frantically, she looked around for a receptacle, saw her box of tissues, ripped the tissues out and promptly vomited into the cardboard. She called for a nurse.

'I've just been sick,' Carole apologized, holding the tissue box, 'but I'm all right now.'

'Don't worry. We'll bring a bowl, you'll be okay.' The nurse exchanged Carole's box for a bowl, smiling sympathetically.

Fifteen minutes later she was sick again. Oh hell, she thought. She felt awful. A half digested, stale flavour of fish lined the back of her ripped gullet. Her stomach waved, rising and sinking while cold sweat washed over her. Carole threw up repeatedly and the minute she vomited she felt sick yet again. There was no escape. She was sick every ten minutes and when she wasn't being sick she was waiting to be sick.

At ten past five, Nick's mother and Joy came to visit her, but after a few minutes they left, feeling helpless and frightened.

'Tell Nick to come' she whimpered.

Carole was still vomiting every ten minutes when Nick finally arrived at seven o'clock clutching a large, expensive bird book under his arm. He sat down on the chair beside her bed, distinctly uncomfortable, and looked at her in hopeless compassion. Then, through her regular bouts of heaving, she heard him mutter something about an RSPB meeting in Leicester that night which he thought he'd like to attend. Carole could not believe it! She wasn't sure what she expected from him, even what help anyone could offer - but she felt badly let down by his seeming lack of care.

After half an hour of unsupportive company, she discharged her husband from duty.

'You might as well go,' she said. And he went.

Throughout Carole's hours of constant sickness, the nurses attended to her caringly, changing her bowl, assisting with any small measure of comfort and offering gentle reassurance. By nine thirty, and still vomiting regularly, her exhausted, empty frame ached all over. She felt totally drained - and yet still she retched. Through her limp tiredness, she was aware of a nurse rather belatedly administering an 'anti-sickness drug' and within minutes Carole was fast asleep.

At three in the morning, she awoke desperately wanting a drink. She wobbled out of bed, her legs like jelly and within seconds a nurse came to steady her.

'Is there anything I can get you?' she asked.

'I'd love a cold glass of milk.'

37

The nurse guided Carole back to bed promising she'd see what she could do. Soon she returned with a full glass of cool, refreshing milk which Carole poured down her throat in one delicious go, no longer caring whether it made her sick or not. It was like nectar from heaven - and didn't make her sick. Then she slid down under the sheets, falling into a deep sleep until the nurses woke her at six o'clock for breakfast.

After a welcome cup of tea and a cautious nibble of a small piece of dry toast, Carole was told to bath and dress for going home. Three bottles of pills were given to her, two being steroid medication and the third an anti-sickness drug - in total, nine pills to be taken daily for the next fourteen days. Her adverse reaction to chemotherapy had been unfortunately dramatic leaving her full of fear in the knowledge that Part B of Chemotherapy 1 was due to be administered next Friday followed by two weeks' reprieve before the cycle repeated itself with Part A of Chemotherapy 2. And so on and so on until Christmas.

On Sunday, Nick flew back to Tanzania. Understandably, it had not been an easy week for either of them and Carole was so depressed that his departure barely made matters worse. Her own parents were probably more helpful than Nick and she allowed herself to be a proper poorly little girl, soaking up their loving care like a small, frightened child.

Friday came and Eunice drove Carole down for Part B of Chemotherapy 1, staying briefly during her initial blood test before leaving.

'I'll be back just after three to take you straight home,' she promised with a parting smile.

This time, the side room to St Mary's Ward was full of women waiting to receive chemotherapy with the main ward already half taken up by in-patients. Carole smiled timidly at the sea of strange faces but isolated herself from their cheerful gossip. How could they sound so happy? she thought as idle, mundane chatter bounced around the ward's annex.

Soon, a nurse ushered them all into the main ward, indicating each patient a bed to lie on.

Carole had never wanted to run away from anything so much in her life before. At lunchtime, she poked and prodded her meal unable to eat a morsel, and then she just lay, waiting in dread, for Dr Khanna to arrive. At three o'clock, he breezed into the ward, and immediately, a discreet efficiency rippled through the air reminding Carole of schooldays when teacher entered the classroom. The nurses bristled busily, fetching trays and trolleys, drips and medication.

Eventually, Dr Khanna and two nurses arrived at Carole's bedside. Desperately she tried to detach herself from reality, to escape somehow, but she was only too aware, as the needle was injected into her arm, of the poisonous drugs easing their way into her body.

Eunice arrived at half past three and they dashed full speed straight to Enderby where Carole hurried to her bedroom with a brown bucket and waited.

Nothing happened.

Five o'clock - still nothing. No sickness! She didn't even feel queasy! For the rest of the night she mentally tiptoed around in trepidation, growing increasingly optimistic but ever cautious. By nine o'clock she felt home and dry. She had obviously built up a huge resistance to the drugs, developed an immunity.

Carole laughed with relief! Just one more week of tablets then two weeks off. She could cope with that. Not only could she cope - but Victoria and Marc were due to arrive to spend their school summer holidays with their mum and grandparents in Enderby. It would be a squeeze in the small house, but it gave Carole the hope and strength to soldier on. All she had to do was re-adjust her thinking and plan that bit further ahead.

Now it was 1984 she had to aim towards. A new year and a new life for 1984.

CHAPTER EIGHT

And Then a Bad Tooth

The children arrived safely, excited by the fact they had travelled unaccompanied, and they were all thrilled to be together again.

Although the steroids were beginning to cause uncomfortable bloating and giddiness, Carole felt tolerably well. Her date for Part A of Chemotherapy 2 was approaching, but at least she felt confident that her initial sickness would not repeat itself.

This time, Joy, Nick's sister, drove Carole down and waited in the side annex while she had her pre-treatment blood test. It revealed a precariously low blood count meaning that she couldn't receive chemotherapy and was told to go home and come again the following Friday.

Victoria and Marc were happy to be with their mother; they were close to their father but he did not involve himself so much with their lives, nor them with his. They told Carole he was still busy bird watching with every spare hour and for the first time in ages, her thoughts turned to Lynn. Of course, with the children now in England, he was totally free of all family commitments or watchful, telling eyes.

Struggling once again with jealousy, Carole worked hard to push hurtful thoughts out of her mind. She had this weird, parallel notion that her cancer was like jealousy, and if she let it take hold of her, consume her, then she was allowing the cancer to do the same. Anyway, how could Lynn - or Nick - knowing that she was there in Leicester enduring chemotherapy after radiotherapy for Hodgkin's Disease, conduct an affair behind her back, now? How on earth could they possibly, with any slight degree of reasonable conscience, continue any infidelity while she was fighting for survival? The idea wasn't even worthy of further thought.

Nick and Carole phoned each other weekly. He voiced concern but didn't sense any urgency to be with his wife. The separation was not binding them more closely and Carole ached to be well again. She had to be patient but agonized over the endless months of treatment still to wade through.

On July 8th, Joy once again accompanied Carole in her second attempt for Part A of Chemotherapy 2, and this time her blood count was acceptable. Joy left, reminding Carole that Eunice would arrive just after three o'clock to take her back and Carole smiled gratefully. This time she felt reasonably calm, believing she had now acquired a resistance to the drugs or that they had been modified to reduce side effects following her initial adverse reaction.

However, when fish was served for lunch again, Carole was unable to do more than pick and prod. Dr Khanna administered the drugs at three o'clock and Eunice arrived shortly after. The two weeks supply of medication had not yet been prepared and they had to wait for them; then Carole was told she needed a chest X-ray. By then it was half past four and as she reached the X-ray clinic a cold, queasy wave of nausea suddenly washed over her. She flew into the nearby toilets and retched violently into the lavatory.

Somehow, Carole managed to have the X-ray taken, but was sick twice more before they reached Eunice's car. Eunice had the brown bucket ready in the back seat, just in case, and they travelled home, Carole clutching it tightly between her knees. As soon as they got back, she took herself to bed, brown bucket by her side and vomited every ten minutes until half past nine.

So she was not immune.

This is what she would have to suffer. Every bone and muscle in her body soon ached from retching. Her stomach, quickly empty of its contents, heaved and gagged, tearing her parched throat but determined to eject every last drop of poison.

The television in her bedroom ploughed through its regular weekly series of the '"A" Team', punctuated periodically with light-hearted adverts - all so far away and oblivious to her sickness.

Carole's mother popped in occasionally to empty the bucket. Carole was aware at one time that it was Marc. The evening just had to be endured. Nothing helped. It was absolute sheer hell and it ended at about nine thirty when her exhausted, dehydrated and hollow body crashed into a begging sleep. At three in the morning, she awoke, craving for the glass of milk ready and waiting, gulped it down in one go and fell straight back to sleep until lunch time.

The following week Carole had Part B of Chemotherapy 2 and suffered no sickness.

Now she realized the pattern although she didn't understand it. The first half, 'part A', made her very sick whereas the second half didn't. However, the steroid medication was making her unwell. Now bloated and overweight, a strange craving for food failed to satisfy an uncomfortable stomach and Carole looked a wreck. A swollen, pale face with red rimmed eyes was heavily circled by dark shadows. Her hair (what there was of it) hung dull and lifeless, her teeth had yellowed, and her stomach was grossly distended. She felt ill, drained and depressed.

On top of all that, Carole was being plagued with recurring bouts of toothache.

Nick arrived on August 23rd and she detected a look of shock on his face when he saw her. Also, Carole's blood count had been consistently low and she was unable to have Part A of Chemotherapy 3 until August 26th.

Accompanied by an apprehensive Nick, he took Carole to the Infirmary for treatment and collected her at half past three. Her sickness followed the predictable course she had now learnt to expect.

Over the weekend, Carole was consumed with a raging, hot toothache and, on Nick's insistence, she visited her dentist first thing Monday morning.

'Hmm,' the dentist frowned, 'I think your problem has been caused by radiotherapy. Really, the tooth needs to come out, but under the circumstances I think you must see the hospital dentist.'

The following week, at Part B of Chemotherapy 3, Carole mentioned the tooth problem to Dr Khanna. He considered an extraction should be safe carefully undertaken with antibiotics and an appointment was made to have the tooth removed a week later.

Sandwiched between the two hospital appointments, Nick and the children left to go back home. Carole was at a dangerously low ebb. Their marriage was far from good and she now felt desolate at losing Victoria and Marc.

Somehow she just had to hang on to the thought of next year; to get well again and go back to Tanzania, rebuild her life and relationship with Nick. But right then, her resistance to anything was nil and she was so depressed it was a struggled just to find the will to live. She was in no state to cope with anything - least of all having a tooth extracted.

As a precaution, the hospital dentist first administered an antibiotic injection to fight off any possible infection, then froze the area around the offending huge, black molar. With the gum deadened, the dentist pulled and twisted, but the obstinate tooth refused to come out. Although Carole could feel no pain, she sensed the tugging and noticed beads of perspiration on the dentist's brow. After about five minutes of fierce wrangling, the dentist finally won the battle - triumphantly boasting a badly diseased molar in his pincers. But Carole's gum was ripped and she needed four stitches before being discharged home.

Over that weekend, she started to develop what seemed to be a cold. On Monday morning, feeling shivery and wheezy and only too aware of the potential seriousness of the common cold in her condition, she went to see her local doctor. It was the first time she'd seen him since that first day of spring when Nick and Carole had astounded him with the news that she had Hodgkin's Disease.

'Come in!' called the doctor. Carole went in and sat down. 'Ah, now how are things?'

Carole explained about the treatment she was undergoing, her low blood count, the tooth extraction and finally, of her shivery flu type symptoms. He nodded without undue concern.

'Take some cough medicine and keep warm,' he advised, scribbling illegibly on a prescription pad. And with that, she left.

The next day, Carole woke up desperately out of breath. Staggering to the bathroom and gasping for air, she gulped down a glass of cold water. Her burning throat felt as if in a strangled grip, and her chest so tight she could hardly breathe. Carole cried out to her mother for help before limping back to bed where she lay, shivering in hot and cold sweats, and gasping for air.

The doctor arrived at lunch time clearly irritated by a house call for the common cold. After a brief examination, he dismissed it as nothing to worry about and left, leaving Carole scared and vulnerable.

By Wednesday, her life seemed to be slowly ebbing away. Her lifeless body shivered and her breathing faint - yet strangely, a part within her felt milky calm. She knew she was dying and a peculiar resignation peacefully blanketed her as she drifted in and out of consciousness. Vaguely in the distance she was aware of her mother, and then Joy, panicking in desperation.

'No, not the doctor - that's no good!'

'Try the hospital, St Mary's Ward…'

'She can't breathe!'

'They're sending an ambulance. Oh, dear God...'

Before long, two heroic pillars of masculine strength enveloped Carole in a warm, red blanket, carried her gently down the stairs and into a waiting ambulance.

Lying in the ambulance, her head slightly raised, she observed how easy it was to see out of those sinister black windows. And as the vehicle gently eased away, she looked at the little terraced house, her childhood home, then saw the church where she and Nick had been married and the school opposite, and she calmly wondered if she would ever see them again.

CHAPTER NINE

Dying

Dr Khanna, with his team of nurses, was ready and waiting. On Carole's arrival, she was whisked away into a small, private room and immediately attended to. One nurse took her temperature and reported it as 103; another registered her pulse at 120; Dr Khanna sounded her chest in between a fast, authoritative deliverance of instructions.

Carole was barely breathing.

But she had stopped fighting, stopped worrying. Skimming thin slivers of air through dry lips, she abandoned herself totally in detached calm to their industrious concern.

'Have you ever had glandular fever?' Dr Khanna asked his patient.

Carole tried to shake her head and offer a negative grunt with muttered wheezings about her tooth extraction and cold.

His dark eyes frowned but he made no comment. Turning to a nurse, he ordered Carole to remain isolated for observation and be transferred to the single ward at the end of St Martha's, which she knew to be the male cancer ward.

In the single annex to St Martha's, and still bristling with organized urgency, the nurses carried out an electrocardiogram, chest X-ray, nose swab, throat swab and blood test. Eventually, she was attached to an intravenous antibiotic drip and left to sleep.

For forty-eight hours, Carole's life hung in the balance. Close friends and family had debated whether to urge Nick to rush over but considered it pessimistic, although he was kept constantly informed of his wife's condition. Dr Khanna monitored Carole closely and consistently but it was two days before she was aware of anything.

There is no doubt that without the immediate care and attention of an efficient, dedicated team of nurses and Dr Khanna, Carole would have died.

'You nearly had me worried there, Mrs Baker,' confessed Dr Khanna eventually.

'What on earth's been happening to me?' Carole asked.

'I think you've had septicaemia through having the tooth taken out with such a low blood count. All other tests have proved negative,' he added by way of explanation.

Barely any the wiser, she drifted away again vaguely aware that she had just pulled through a life threatening crisis.

The next few days followed with gradual improvement aided by a four pint blood infusion and an antibiotic drip. Carole was now able to enjoy a steady stream of relieved visitors though much talking still rendered her exhausted. One thing she wasn't short of was friends. But neither Carole nor anyone else had heard from Nick since he'd last been told of her condition. It didn't help moments of self-pity and, apart from feeling neglected and rejected by him, two other things in particular made her feel very sorry for herself.

For a start, she had really wanted to visit the Home Life Exhibition at Leicester's Granby Halls, coincidentally just opposite her hospital bed. Every night as she lay there in her single room, she could hear the sounds of parking traffic, slamming of car doors and the laughter of happy, healthy people going to the exhibition. She sulkily visualized loving families redesigning their home, young couples planning a first house and giggling children clinging to a variety of free samples.

On top of that, Victoria's fourteenth birthday was the following Tuesday. The first one ever without her mother. Carole pictured the three of them back in Dar es Salaam, Victoria excitedly opening presents and enjoying fun and teasing from her brother and father, rounded off with a special birthday dinner at the end of the day.

Carole felt bitterly excluded.

But a new strength was just beginning to emerge. Ill as she still was, a tenuous thread of determination would occasionally course through her body, a determination to fight on, get well, win back her marriage and somehow wage this war to its ultimate and triumphant end. If it had been 'her time' to die, she reflected philosophically, surely she would have died a week ago? But instead, she had been given a reprieve and within it, there seemed a symbolic message of hope.

By the Saturday, Carole was weak but walking again. The nurses washed her hair and helped freshen her for moving to St Mary's ward. At last, Nick phoned the hospital and Carole was allowed to take the call on the ward.

'You should have been here, Nick,' she said.

'What's the point in dashing over if you're there in hospital?' he argued, and carried on with everyday conversation that stretched distance and understanding between them even further.

The nurses, though, were fantastic. They had all the time in the world to offer care and company; they had patience to listen, strength to support and encouragement to carry her on. Carole needed their help, emotionally as well as physically.

On Friday 23rd September, after having been in hospital for ten days, Carole was considered well enough to return home. Her arm felt strangely free from the restriction of an intravenous drip; both arms had been employed to avoid excessive bruising - but the result was nevertheless two, very sore arms. Her head felt giddy, her legs weak and her stomach constantly nauseous. But as she walked down the ward to meet her parents who had come to take her home, she saw all the chemotherapy patients arriving for their treatment. Carole gave them a wave and they smiled back. However ill she had been and however rough she still felt - just at that moment she wouldn't have swapped for the world!

But unfortunately, there were only two weeks before Part A of Chemotherapy 4. As Carole joined the 'regulars' in the side annex of the cancer ward, she was plagued with questions as to what had happened. She related her story to them and they replied with their own case histories leaving Carole tremendously comforted and inspired by their courage.

There was Sue, a young girl of eighteen, who had just got engaged when she learned she, too, had Hodgkin's Disease. At the other end of the scale was Doris, an elderly patient of Hodgkin's Disease being treated for her third relapse. Doris proudly boasted that she had been the very first patient in Leicester to receive chemotherapy eight years previously. Then there was Jean and Angela with breast cancer, Barbara with ovarian cancer and Roberta with lymphoma.

There were ten of them altogether and Carole learned that they had different kinds of chemotherapy with varying reactions. She also learned how united they all felt in their battle for survival and how it helped to share the dread and fear.

However, it didn't lessen the side-effects.

Eunice came to collect Carole at three thirty and it was back to the familiar dash home and up to her bedroom with the brown bucket. It seemed nothing could ease the relentless vomiting and the martyr in her wished Nick could witness how she was suffering. He was due to arrive in a few days time - neatly avoiding his wife at her worst.

As it happened, Carole was still very low when he arrived but it made no difference one way or the other. It seemed he was particularly eager to take on a hectic round of social visits, thereby deliberately avoiding just the two of them being together. Admittedly, it was fairly cramped at Carole's parents' house, and it did feel almost too risky alone in each other's company - there were too many things unsaid, too many feelings unspoken and not enough time to cope with the backlog of pent up emotion. It was safer not to start.

Carole's depression was dragging him down. He seemed to fidget constantly, always frantic to be on the move and even over a cup of coffee she would watch him restlessly drum his fingers on the table.

But she was to load him with even greater despair before he could escape back to Africa.

Nick took Carole to hospital the following Friday for Part B of Chemotherapy 4. As this was the half that didn't make her sick, Nick was quite happy to hang around and take her back home a few hours later. When Dr Khanna came to administer the drugs, he hesitated at the foot of the bed browsing through her medical notes.

'Hmm,' he murmured soberly.

Carole froze. Surely the blood test had been okay - what did 'hmm' mean? Slowly, he moved his eyes away from his papers and fixed them onto his patient.

'I think we ought to consider the possibility of nine chemotherapies.'

She didn't care why.

Death at that moment would have been infinitely preferable to additional chemotherapy.

Carole couldn't take it and burst into tears.

'Tears don't move me, Mrs Baker,' he said ruthlessly and busied away leaving apologetic nurses to administer the drugs. The blackest cloud of depression swamped her in a more endless tunnel than her disease. It couldn't be real. It wasn't fair. What had she done to deserve this?

Nick didn't know how to cope with her. What sympathy he had seemed overpowered by his own uncomfortable distress of feeling unable to help.

He must have been relieved to end his stay.

A few days later Gary and Eunice drove them to Heathrow. Carole behaved like a clinging child, snivelling in the back seat and twisting sodden tissues around her fingers. Periodically, Nick would pat her hand as a reassuring gesture but it had been a difficult time together and now Carole resented his health and freedom bitterly. It wasn't just losing Nick again. It was where he was going to. Even the knowledge that he would be back for Christmas with the children couldn't ease the heartache. She so wanted to see Pinky. It felt a life time since she'd been home; her treatment wasn't moving quickly enough and she couldn't see an end to it. Carole had already endured chemotherapy for nearly five months - and yet, with the threat of an extended course, she wasn't even halfway through. And there was something else Carole had to check out with him before he left.

'We're just friends,' he said, 'Lynn feels very sorry over everything that has happened - but there is absolutely nothing between us, in fact I rarely see her. I just want you to get well again.'

Carole didn't probe further. She needed to believe him.

CHAPTER TEN

A Spiritual Journey

On Friday 4th November Carole went to the hospital for Part A of Chemotherapy 5 accompanied by Marianne, a small blonde with an easy smile and inquisitive personality (and the author of this book). Marianne's husband, Pete, was an old colleague of Nick's and they had both taken it upon themselves to help where they could. Also, as a freelance writer, Marianne was in the throes of compiling research on psychic healing for a local magazine and felt she could add substance to her article if she were able to talk amongst other cancer patients.

As it happened, she unearthed some quite astounding revelations from two of the group that neither Carole nor Marianne had anticipated.

Firstly, Doris, the elderly Hodgkin's Disease patient being treated for her third relapse, believed she had 'died' twice during her illness. On both occasions, she had been welcomed 'on the other side' by her mother who had passed away many years previously. But the greeting was short lived as Doris was told to 'go back', that it 'wasn't yet time' - though her mother promised she would be there, waiting for her, when it was.

This was seconded by Barbara, a plump, comfortable and strangely contented woman with ovarian cancer. She too, spoke of having 'died', and described her sensation of travelling down a tunnel - aware of light, peace and love at the end, but, sensing or being guided that it was not yet 'her time', had returned.

Doris nodded.

'That's right,' she said softly, as much to herself as anyone else.

No-one spoke for a while. Carole had goose pimples running up and down her spine. One or two of the others seemed to nod, too, and there was no doubt their experiences were totally believed and understood by their captive listeners.

Carole suddenly thought back to when she'd been so ill with septicaemia - the milky calm, the peaceful resignation… had all that been the first steps of a near death experience? She felt privileged they had shared their stories, and Marianne had just collected two more personal revelations way beyond the call of research.

As soon as Carole was called to receive treatment, Marianne left with the promise of them both going to visit a healer she had found in a few days time.

Later that afternoon, Eunice rushed Carole home at record breaking speed for her five hours of sickness. Part B of Chemotherapy 5 fell a week later, on November 11th. It was a dismal, drizzly day and Carole was grateful to have yet another friend, Karen, who had travelled up from Chelmsford to visit, stay with her until it was time to go home. In the event, she was doubly grateful as it turned out to be an endlessly long day, waiting from her initial test at nine o'clock until four o'clock for treatment. And then, when she was eventually called for therapy, a doctor she had never seen before struggled for about fifteen minutes butchering her arm for a vein to inject the drugs.

'The vein's collapsed,' he finally said in exasperation.

A nurse wandered off to rectify the problem and returned with a large glass of sherry. By five o'clock, and with treatment now finally administered through a largely dilated blood vessel, Karen and Carole finally left to go home. They both felt stale and tired and Carole's arm was very sore.

Meanwhile, Marianne had arranged for Carole to visit a local spiritual healer to sample the products of her research first hand. Lillian opened the door with a welcoming smile, and Carole was relieved to see she looked a normal, attractive middle aged lady with neither horns nor halo as evidence of supernatural powers. A reassuring warmth emanated from her as she led Carole into a small, cosily lit side room leaving Marianne to browse through magazines in the kitchen.

Lillian was then joined by Ann who Carole took to be a novice healer, purely on account of her slender youth, and they both got her to lie on a red blanketed couch. The room was so small, there was only just enough space for the bed and two healers, but with the soft lighting, red blanket and heavy, maroon curtains, Carole felt encompassed in warmth. Lillian stood one side and Ann the other, and as Carole closed her eyes, she became aware of their deep breathing - no doubt a preliminary exercise to healing thought. A slight movement made her aware that, although they weren't actually touching her, their hands were silently gliding a few inches over her body.

Suddenly, Carole had the irresistible urge to giggle. The whole episode struck her as absurd. What on earth was she doing there? Never having had any inclination to anything remotely 'alternative' before, she was now, literally, in the hands of spiritual healers. But they were genuinely caring, and she certainly received a sense of peace as well as some intriguing information from them before she left.

Once outside and in the car, Marianne was impatient to know what had happened.

'Well?' she quizzed.

'It was relaxing,' Carole offered, 'and they said my next scan would be clear, but nothing miraculous happened - except maybe when they told me what I'd been in my past life.'

'Your *past* life? What were you then?'

'A nun.'

For a few seconds, Marianne gaped, speechless, then slowly an infectious grin spread across her face as both of them started to laugh. For what seemed absolutely ages, they just fell about in a fit of giggles, holding their aching sides, tears streaming down their faces at the comedy of this unlikely reincarnation.

Carole hadn't laughed for weeks, and now she wondered if perhaps this was, in a way, healing.

Unfortunately, there wasn't a scrap of humour left 48 hours later as Eunice drove her to the hospital for Part A of Chemotherapy 6. Carole was already heaving as she parked the car. Gripped in icy panic, she clung on to Eunice's arm.

'I can't do it. I can't bear it any more!'

Eunice tried to comfort her and finally prised Carole out of the car with verbal determination and assurance. But still she was panic stricken, every step seeming a leaden effort towards death row. Eunice was more an inseparable friend than sister-in-law, and promised to stay by her side all day.

A nurse told Carole that she was booked for a body scan and without the slightest faith in the psychic healer's prediction, she went down to the X-ray department full of dread.

For fifteen minutes, she struggled with the preliminary aniseed flavoured liquid to be taken prior to the scan and left it hovering high in her stomach.

She felt very sick.

The body scan completed, Carole returned to the ward still gripped in terror. Eunice never left her side, undoubtedly worried about Carole's mental state and suspecting, quite rightly, that she would bolt given half a chance.

A nurse indicated a bed for her to lie on down the bottom end of the ward, and as she walked towards it, she passed a young couple both oblivious to what was going on around them. She was lying in bed, still, waxen and barely conscious. He was sitting next to her, holding her hand, tears streaming down his face.

This nightmare was unreal. This was hell. Why oh why? Such grief weighted on Carole in pity. For the girl, for him, for herself.... She climbed onto the bed, but as soon as the nurse approached with the tray of syringes, Carole threw up.

But still the treatment had to be endured. There was no way out of it. Only through it. Dr Khanna hardly said a word, making no reference to the extended number of chemotherapies, and Carole didn't ask. As soon as the drugs had been administered, Eunice rushed her back home for the expected ritual.

The next day, Nick phoned.

He told his wife he'd been bird watching in the Pugu Forest, that Marc and Victoria were fine, the dogs great and the weather superb. In all, he was having a good time. He offered a few words of sympathy but Carole could sense his thoughts were there, in Tanzania.

He seemed a million miles away and Carole was consumed with loneliness.

Meanwhile, Marianne had unearthed another healer.

This time, a professional holistic practitioner, Win Wood, who claimed to combine healing prayer with qualified reflexology and aromatherapy. Carole meekly allowed Marianne to instigate a healing session for her and they drove over to Win's rambling, old farmhouse near Loughborough on Thursday 8th December, the day before Part B of Chemotherapy 6.

Win was - is, a petite, brightly dressed lady with child like enthusiasm, and alert, penetrating eyes. Her face lit up with greeting as she ushered Carole and Marianne eagerly into her warmly lit living room. As with Lillian, the house seemed to glow with reds and pinks and maroons, but the farmhouse boasted spaciousness brimming with antique furniture and flowers.

Immediately, Carole felt safe.

After a cup of tea and a chat, Win led Carole into the 'healing room', just another spacious room full of pink and red with an abundance of flowers spilling over in every conceivable space.

A reclining chair served as a therapy couch, and as she lay there to the muted strains of Eastern music she poured out her fears, pains and grievances unashamedly. Win firstly worked on her feet, listening attentively. Slowly she relaxed, aware of the faint smells of sandalwood, jasmine and lavender. She could hear her talking gently, was aware of soft movements as she worked through her healing procedure - but Carole must have drifted away. Apparently, over an hour had gone by before they rejoined Marianne.

Shortly afterwards they left, Marianne commenting that Carole looked positively radiant. Win Wood gave her a meditation cassette and told her she had nothing to fear.

In fact, Carole truly felt she had nothing to fear. Whether or not there was actually anything in the healing, she was definitely more relaxed than she had been for months. Even the next day, for Part B of Chemotherapy 6, she remained calm.

The Friday patients were all talking in the side annex of St Mary's ward, waiting for the routine blood test results before being called to go on a bed for treatment, when Doris was asked to have a talk with the doctor. Twenty minutes later, she came back beaming, her lean, sallow face flushed with happiness.

'I'm going to meet my mum!' she laughed.

They all stared at her, unsure of what she was inferring.

'I'm not having any more treatment! There's no more they can do...'

Carole felt uncomfortable at her perverse delight, but Doris was so genuinely pleased it seemed cruel not to share it with her. Slowly, hesitantly, they all began to express cautious pleasure, but it was a poignant reminder that sometimes nothing further could be done. It also made Carole aware that she desperately wanted to live. Soon, it was her turn to hear some good news.

'Well, Mrs Baker, you'll be pleased to know the results from your scan were clear.'

Carole looked into the dark, sober eyes of Dr Khanna.

'What does that mean?'

'It means you no longer have any trace of cancer left in your body.'

No reaction.

She didn't dare. His words lay on the surface like oil on water.

Cancer gone? No longer any trace in her body? Did this mean she was cured? Carole searched his face for confirmation and saw he was almost smiling.

'We may consider just one more chemotherapy sufficient,' he continued as his words began to sink in.

She was cured! She no longer had cancer! Now she could understand his detached, unemotional manner; his brusque professionalism. He could never afford to become personally involved or he would be emotionally drained. The work was demanding enough without taking on board the inevitable gains and losses. But right then, there was no denying his look of hope and Carole instantly forgave him for every curt remark and unfeeling gesture he had ever made.

As soon as he moved on, Carole whispered to the nurses,

'Do I have to have any more treatment?'

'Well, always the decision is yours, you know,' but they cautiously remained reluctant to impart advice.

'Oh, Eunice!' Carole laughed on the way back home, 'I can't wait to tell Nick!'

Eunice grinned back at her, as thrilled as she was. Carole's parents, too, were so happy for their daughter - and no doubt for themselves. It couldn't have been easy having her come and live with them after years of independence, and especially under such unfortunate conditions. But Carole's real excitement was in telling Nick and she must have rehearsed her planned conversation with him a hundred times! She would telephone him about nine o'clock British time, that would be about midnight there. Marc and Victoria would be asleep, giving her undisturbed privacy in which to relate her news. This, she knew, would give them some tangible reality to build on, a foundation of real hope for the future, a huge step forward in being a united family once again.

Carole forced herself to last out until nine, then, with trembling fingers, dialled the long list of digits to link her with Dar es Salaam. The line rang out and out. Puzzled, she tried again. No answer. Impatient for him to pick up the receiver, she dialled again, very slowly, carefully, making doubly sure she had the correct numbers... but still it just rang out and out and out. Momentarily deflated, Carole waited ten minutes and tried again. Nothing. That's weird, she thought. Surely he must be in? And anyway, she'd rung so persistently even Marc and Victoria would have answered her call had they been there. Where were they all?

Carole must have tried seven or eight times during the course of the evening, making it virtually throughout the night there - but every time, it just rang out unanswered. In the end, she had to give up and go to sleep.

The next morning, she phoned first thing but still no reply. She tried constantly throughout the whole of Saturday, all Saturday night and all Sunday. No answer.

And Carole felt so flat now. All her excitement had dissolved into disappointed anger. All she could do was phone him at work early on Monday morning.

'Nick! I've been trying to call you all weekend! Where have you been?' Carole exclaimed as she finally heard his voice on the other end of the line.

'Er, nowhere...' he muttered.

'The results from my scan are clear - I no longer have any trace of cancer! I've been bursting to tell you since Friday night but you just haven't been there!'

'I think the line was out of order,' he said, 'but that's great! Now you can put it all behind you.'

After she'd put the phone down, she still felt flat. The conversation hadn't followed any of her rehearsed fantasies, and although he had obviously been pleased for her, he hadn't shown a thrilled excitement for *them*.

Obviously Carole still had to work at rebuilding their relationship and thoughts turned now towards Christmas and the new year. The next 'additional' set of chemotherapy was due on January 6th and 13th - and if

Dr Khanna followed his last inclination, he may well consider that sufficient. Then she could plan her return to Tanzania. She understood it had been difficult for Nick and the children and had to make allowances for any disappointment she felt between Nick and herself. After all, it hadn't been a good year for any of them. They would shortly be arriving to spend Christmas with them. Nothing was going to spoil that.

Carole resolved to discard all negative doubts about her marriage. It was time to look forward, not back. It was time to concentrate on being a good mother and loving wife again. Her health was naturally very poor from the treatment, let alone the cancer - but with every scrap of energy she could muster, she traipsed around Leicester carefully indulging in lavish presents for everyone - mum, dad, Eunice, Marc, Victoria and Nick.

One morning, having the house quietly to herself, she was wrapping up some presents, humming along with the festive carols from the radio when she heard a clatter of post tumbling through the letter box. Eagerly rushing to sort through the inevitable delivery of Christmas cards, she was delighted to see a letter from Marc.

How lovely! Carole opened it to see immediately that he had managed to fill almost one side of airmail paper, no mean achievement for Marc! But on reading all his news, her mouth suddenly went dry. She read the same sentence over and over again, then, trembling, Carole let the letter hang limply in her hands.

'...at half-term we had a great time! We all went to Mufindi and I camped in Lynn's garden...'

CHAPTER ELEVEN

A New Start

Two days before Christmas, Nick arrived with the children, their exuberance swamping any other emotions until later. They were preparing for bed when Carole confronted Nick with what she knew.

'You're blowing it up out of all proportion,' he insisted. 'It was purely a bird watching day with a brief one night stop-over. Lynn is just a friend. Nothing more.' He put his arm around Carole and gave her a big hug, somehow diluting the significance of it all until she believed it was all a figment of her suspicious imagination.

Nick now appeared thrilled over his wife's scan results and as impatient as she was for her return. He said that he'd asked his company for new accommodation near to The Saltpans, and it looked as if they should be in their new house for when she joined him.

Christmas morning was thoroughly enjoyed in traditional generous spirit, all of them delighted with their gifts, followed by well-wishing phone calls to friends and family and an early glass of sherry. By the time they sat down to a festive turkey dinner, Carole's Christmas mood was glowing with wine and happiness.

'Here's to good health!' beamed Carole's father and they clinked their glasses together in unison, wishing each one in turn a 'Happy Christmas!'

Later that afternoon, Nick and Carole escaped to their bedroom, both to give Carole's parents some space and for she and Nick to watch Superman on their own television.

'Would you like some trifle?' Carole asked Nick.

'Mmm, yes please.' He stretched out on the bed in comfort, a suggestive smile spreading across his face. She winked back at him and went downstairs.

As she scooped a generous helping of the creamy dessert into a dish, she overheard Victoria telling her grandma about a recent trip to Mufindi. Carole just stopped in her tracks and froze. Her back was turned towards them so they couldn't have noticed the blood instantly drain from her face. She took a few deep breaths, composed herself and, smiling sweetly at Victoria, said,

'When did you last go to Mufindi, then?'

Victoria shuffled uncomfortably, as if under some instruction not to tell her mother.

'Er...two weekends ago,' she admitted reluctantly.

That was not half-term.

That was after half-term.

Two weekends ago was that weekend Carole had spent hours and hours trying to phone Nick to tell him she was free of cancer. Throwing a faint smile, Carole went upstairs carrying the large dish of trifle. A threatening, violent temper was simmering dangerously in the pit of her stomach. She had never felt anger like this before. It started to rise, blazing - yet acidly controlled. The injustice of it all overwhelmed her. That special weekend when she had been overjoyed with her scan results, bursting to share it with Nick - and all that time he had been in Mufindi with Lynn, *again*. And he had lied to her.

Carole opened the bedroom door.

'Did you go to Mufindi a couple of weekends ago?'

Nick stiffened momentarily.

'Why?'

'Because Victoria said you'd all been there.'

'Well, yes...'

'And you lied to me about the telephone being out of order so that I didn't know.'

'I just didn't want you to worry that there was anything going on. It was just a bird watching trip.'

'And you stayed at Lynn's?'

'She offered accommodation.'

The memory of her trying to ring him that weekend, the frustration, the confusion, the disappointment now rose within her. She exploded, hurling the trifle full pelt into his face, splattering fruit, jelly and cream all over him and all over the wall behind him.

Nick just sat there on the bed, silently staring at his wife out of shock, or fear, or indifference, trifle trickling foolishly down his face. The eruption of dessert, like Carole's anger, now spent.

Christmas Day was ruined.

Carole felt drained and bitter. And the hardest part of all was carrying on in front of the family as if nothing had happened.

In 1982 Nick had told her he loved another woman; in 1983 she'd been treated for cancer. 1984 was just around the corner but now, instead of optimistically looking forward to a New Year, she was full of apprehension. The rest of Christmas was spent perfunctorily visiting friends and relatives, acting outwardly cheerful but inwardly feeling a mess. The New Year came and Nick joined Carole for Part A of Chemotherapy 7 on January 6th. This was postponed owing to a low blood count.

On Thursday 12th January, she had an appointment to see Dr Khanna to discuss her future. He confirmed the scan had been clear and reiterated his opinion that maybe, just maybe, one more treatment of chemotherapy might be sufficient but that she would need blood tests and a thorough examination at two monthly intervals for the first year. He was prepared to allow her doctor in Dar es Salaam carry out alternate tests, meaning that Dr Khanna himself wanted to see her every four months.

Carole felt now that she couldn't even try to make a go of her marriage until she was back in Tanzania. The only hope was that once she was there, as a wife and mother, she and Nick would start to rebuild a loving relationship. It was futile in Enderby to give it a fair trial.

On Friday 13th January, chemotherapy was again postponed owing to a persistent low blood count. Three days later, Nick and the children flew back to Dar es Salaam with hopeful promises of Carole joining them within the month. Impatience ate at her, she needed to be with them, she had to get back... had to eliminate Lynn's very existence from their marriage.

Lillian, the first healer that Carole visited with Marianne, had started a Spiritual Awareness Class on Wednesday afternoons and Marianne and Carole decided they would like to attend. The groups were designed to train them in meditation, colour, aura, prayer, healing and tuning in to the 'Great White Light'. They were both sceptical over many of their psychic claims, but the afternoons nevertheless gave Carole a strong thread of comfort in the genuine offer of spiritual love - and usually provided her and Marianne with a giggly, post-class chuckle!

Chemotherapy was postponed two further times - January 20th and 27th owing to a low blood count, and Carole questioned Dr Khanna as to what this might imply. However, he seemed unperturbed, explaining that it was a natural side effect from treatment.

'We'll leave it another two weeks,' he said, 'and if it's still too low we might consider forgetting chemotherapy.'

Carole tried to quell an urge for optimism. She knew Dr Khanna was always over cautious with his patients and as he was reluctant for her to go back to Tanzania at all, he would be extremely hesitant to cut back on treatment. And as it happened, her restrained hope proved a wise omen. A few days later Carole developed a chesty cold.

Frightened, shivery and with a temperature of 101, she dosed herself with pills and went straight to bed. Drawing on all the healing prayer and 'Great White Light' that she could muster, her fear of septicaemia with such a low blood count were, nevertheless, dangerously real.

Miraculously, the next day Carole was much better. (Could it have been the prayers?) And it meant that at last, she could finally fight infection.

On Friday 10th February, Eunice went with her for yet another attempt at chemotherapy. The fact that she had fought off a cold so easily made her think that maybe her blood count was up - which would mean treatment. It had been so long since the last chemotherapy that Carole felt unprepared and now she was consumed with terror. She was nauseous and shaking when Dr Khanna called her onto the bed and he drew the curtains around them for privacy. He looked at her soberly, which she took as an indication treatment was going ahead.

'Well, your blood count's still low, Mrs Baker,' Dr Khanna pensively stroked his chin.

'I had a bit of a cold last week,' Carole admitted.

'Hmm. That's probably why it's down. Well, so much time has now passed since your last treatment that I can't see any point in giving you further chemotherapy.'

Carole hardly dared breathe. She wanted him to hurry up and go away before he changed his mind - yet she needed to know for sure exactly what he was saying.

'When can I go back to Tanzania?'

'When your blood count is over 4 and that should happen naturally in the course of time. I want to see you in a month. Then, if I'm satisfied with you, you can go back.'

With that, he moved on. Carole collapsed with relief in a crumpled heap of tears. A nurse sat on the bed next to her and gave her a comforting hug while poor Eunice, craning in anguish through a slit in the curtains and convinced she'd just received devastating news, could contain herself no longer.

'Has he been upsetting you again?' she demanded, forcing a prohibited entry through the screens.

'It's over,' was all Carole could whimper.

The nurse looked at Eunice, nodding happily in confirmation. Eunice started to smile and as Carole looked up at them both through her tears, a huge, silly grin spread from ear to ear.

'It's over, it's over, it's over.'

CHAPTER TWELVE

Back to Dar es Salaam

The relief continued to grow throughout the day. Carole hadn't realized how much the last chemotherapy had been hanging over her until it was removed and now she just kept absorbing Dr Khanna's words with renewed bursts of happiness.

She rang Nick and the children who were thrilled, all three of them impatient now for her imminent return. Carole's parents were just as delighted as their daughter and the whole house was filled with a long forgotten madcap playfulness. Carole and Eunice went out in the evening for a celebratory drink and Carole finally rolled into bed very late, very tipsy and still silly with relief. The next two weeks were filled with a round of carefree visits to friends and family interwoven with shopping trips where Carole started to build up a new summer wardrobe for her return home. In addition to summery T-shirts and shorts, she stocked up on practical domestic items, presents for the children and leather chews for Kizzy and Pinky. She couldn't wait to see Pinky again! It was hard to believe that the last time she had seen her had been on Mothering Sunday almost twelve months previously when she'd left to go to Nairobi for her biopsy.

On Monday 12th March, Carole had an appointment with Dr Khanna for extensive blood tests and examination, followed the next day with further tests, an X-ray plus a list of worrying guidelines in the event of her being discharged. She was told to telephone the hospital on Wednesday for the results.

On Tuesday night Carole could hardly sleep. She tossed and turned with thoughts of going back home, only to check herself that it might not happen yet. The next day finally arrived, and with pounding heart, she asked Dr Khanna for her results.

She was clear.

Now she could finally go back to Tanzania. By lunchtime, Carole had her air ticket, a single flight from Heathrow leaving Sunday 1st April (unbelievably Mothering Sunday!), stopping at Cairo and Khartoum to arrive in Dar es Salaam seven o'clock Monday morning. All just fourteen days away.

Now Carole's round of social calls became sentimental farewells and thank yous rather than the previous celebrations. She knew she would never have survived without the enormous support and love of her friends and family. It was an emotional time winding down her stay, for however much she desperately wanted to be back in Tanzania, she had grown deeply close to many of her loyal supporters. She would miss them terribly. Without realizing it at the time, Carole's very last evening in England was spent most poignantly with Eunice watching the newly released film 'Champion's Story', the true biographical account of Bob Champion's triumph over cancer to finally win the Grand National horse race.

The film, with John Hurt as Bob Champion, was so incredibly similar to Carole's own story; the diagnosis, the treatment, the chemotherapy, steroids and depression, that she and Eunice cried throughout. And his final conquering of the cancer, to then go forward and win the Grand National - proving in essence the real victory was to overcome and succeed against all odds, was a sensitive reminder that she, too, might still have challenges to face. Their eyes were still red as they hugged goodbye. Wonderful Eunice. Carole would miss her.

On Sunday, Carole's parents drove their daughter to Heathrow. What would life be like for them with her gone? It had been a traumatic time for them. Obviously, they were overjoyed that Carole was supposedly 'cured' of Hodgkin's Disease, that treatment was over and that she was finally going back to her family but how eerily quiet the house would be without her - the phone constantly ringing, visitors forever passing by. Carole knew she had disrupted their previous peace and quiet, but could they easily adjust back to their old bland normality? There had been a few laughs, a few tears and lots of love. In a way, Carole would be sorry to go.

But mixed up with all her nostalgia were thoughts of Africa. How would it feel to stand on Tanzanian soil again? What would the new house be like? How would the children react to their mother being home again? Could Carole and Nick be as close and happy together as they had once been? And would Pinky remember her?

Mum squeezed her daughter tightly as Carole made a move to board the plane.

'Do take care, love,' she urged, smiling with watery eyes. Carole hugged her with a deeply felt love and gratitude.

'I will, don't worry...'

Then Carole turned to her dad and gave him a hug.

'Bye dad, look after mum - and remember, I'll be back again soon!'

And quickly she walked away. She was not just walking away from them; she was walking away from cancer, from chemotherapy, from a year of trauma. It was over - Carole was going back home.

Over sixteen hours later, the familiar coastline of Kenya became recognizable. Hundreds of kilometres of sandy beaches stretched interminably along the eastern coast of Kenya, over Lamu, Malindi and Mombassa with Mount Kilimanjaro to the west, and then down over the Tanzanian border, following the curve of the Indian Ocean as slowly the plane started to descend over Dar es Salaam.

It was almost as if the season of time had lurched forward four or five months; no longer was it the cold, damp, grey English climate. Bright sunshine and blue sky scorched the dusty ground below. A shimmering heat rushed up to meet the circling plane as they made for their final descent and landing; thin, black bodies with khaki shorts and sandals could now be seen swarming industriously around the air terminal building. It all seemed so familiar - like yesterday, and yet like a hundred years ago.

'It's great to have you back,' said Nick as he swung Carole round, beaming broadly. 'Marc and Victoria are waiting outside the Arrival Terminal.'

And then they were all together, the four of them, crying, laughing, hugging, the heat of the early African sun beating down, filling Carole with a long forgotten warmth. Once in the car, Nick explained that the children had first to be driven to school, but that they - she and Nick, would then make their way over to their new home. They had only moved in the previous week, and he warned Carole it was still a bit 'upside down'. But Carole didn't care. She leaned back in the car feeling tired, jet lagged, but indescribably happy. Looking out of the window, she'd forgotten how parched everywhere could look. Black women waddled flat footed down the side of the dusty track wrapped in colourful kangas - some with a small child cocooned on their backs, others with huge baskets balanced on their heads. Marc and Victoria chatted incessantly in the back of the car while Nick tried to drive one handed, his left hand resting on his wife's. They drove to the school and, as the children got out, Carole noticed how much they had grown in the last year. They seemed to belong in Africa, and now their self assurance gave them a maturity she hadn't been aware of in Enderby. Marc's thin brown limbs had developed muscles, and although he had always been much smaller than his sister, he was now the same height and certainly much broader. Protective and confident, he grinned warmly,

'It's great to have you back, mum.'

Victoria, too, smiled and kissed her mum. She, in contrast to Marc, seemed slimmer and very beautiful, a sylph like elegance emerging briefly behind adolescence.

Nick and Carole then drove on to their new home, a large bungalow situated in a modern estate of just nine other houses. With euphoria akin to newly weds, Nick pulled onto the drive in an atmosphere of sensual anticipation.

'Here we are! This is it, you're home.'

But Carole had thoughts of embracing another before Nick… and would she remember her? Carole vaguely noticed cardboard boxes piled high and stacks of books in fallen down piles in the hall - but, ignoring it all, her instincts led her straight to the kitchen.

Pinky!

Carole cried instantly as Pinky leapt immediately off her blanket, twisting and wriggling in uncontrollable excitement towards her. Her long tail crashed from side to side, she jumped up, she licked her, she gave Carole her face, then her bottom, rolled onto the floor, collapsed onto her back and in total abandonment offered Carole her soft, golden belly for emotional fulfilment.

She had remembered her.

Carole crouched down and hugged Pinky, weeping and caressing her, both of them hungry to satisfy a year long wait of heart weary love.

Then Kizzy, their other 'outside' dog came in with Jade, one of her latest pups, and Carole greeted them affectionately as the less nostalgic cats scurried nervously away.

Finally, Carole turned round to face a patiently waiting Nick.

CHAPTER THIRTEEN

And Depression

The 'honeymoon' lasted a week.

It didn't really fade away, but inevitably, life became more realistic - and hard work.

The house was in total chaos. Nick had just bundled miscellaneous belongings into boxes without order or labels, making it impossible to find anything. Admittedly, he had been busy working throughout the move but now it was left for Carole to sort out. She still tired easily and the prospect of so much unpacking was daunting.

However, the house itself was spacious and light with excellent air conditioning - an invaluable advantage in Dar es Salaam, and they also had a new African house-boy called Ali, a cheerful, middle-aged native employed to undertake various domestic tasks. Also, local neighbours came round to introduce themselves and Carole enjoyed returning their visits, especially in the long, daytime hours where an unexpected loneliness had started to creep in. But they, understandably, were detached from and uninvolved in her recent illness, leaving it a private trauma for Carole to work through alone.

Of course she was thrilled to be back; after all, it was all she'd dreamt of for a year and she was happy to be with Nick and the children again. It was a physical and emotional achievement proving she had, hopefully, beaten cancer and survived her husband's affair. But it was not without it's problems. Perhaps Carole's expectations were too high; maybe weakness had left her over sensitive. Certainly she knew nothing then of 'post-cancer depression', but she kept breaking down in tears for the most trivial of reasons making everyone tiptoe around her with wary unease.

After three weeks, it was obvious Carole had lapsed into severe depression. She felt so apologetic and guilty, like a spoilt child who can never be satisfied. Nick was totally perplexed and at a loss as to how to help, no doubt thinking it was him. It wasn't him. It wasn't Lynn - that was behind them. It wasn't the marriage, that was okay. It wasn't Africa, it was great to be back. It wasn't the children, it was good to be with them. She didn't feel ill... so what was wrong with her? How dare she feel sad? How could she possibly be depressed?

A regular routine became established. Nick and the children would leave the house before seven o'clock every morning for work and school. Due to the climate in Dar es Salaam, the day would start early and end early to avoid working in intense afternoon humidity. After they had gone, Carole would potter around doing menial tasks, or sort out another box from the inexhaustible unpacked cartons, and then maybe later pop round to a neighbour for coffee.

On one such morning, Carole was in the kitchen just staring out of the window at the sun scorched garden, too dry yet to work on and looking more like barren scrubland. She must work on that soon, she thought idly. Suddenly, her heart seemed so heavy and the ache dragged through her body like a physical pain. Ripples of memory washed over her in a mixture of grief and longing; Dr Khanna, Eunice, mum and dad, St Mary's ward, all the other patients, the spiritual awareness classes, her friends... all so indelibly etched on her mind. Carole felt so alone, in mourning for all she'd lost instead of happy for what she'd gained.

'Oh Pinky!' she cried, falling down onto the floor beside the dog, 'What's happening? Why do I feel like this?'

Poor, loyal Pinky, so sensitive to Carole's every mood and hardly having left her side since she'd come back, didn't know what to do. She licked Carole with concern in her velvet eyes, sensing her sorrow and offering her paw as a shared gesture of compassionate fellow feeling.

'I love you, Pinky. What would I do without you?' And as Carole buried her damp face into the dog's fur, she vowed then that whatever might happen in the future, she would never leave her again. She would always be with her - until the day one of them died.

Naturally, things had changed domestically while Carole had been away, too, which added to her dejection.

The children had grown very independent, not thinking to tell their mum whether or not they would be returning home after school, not bothering to consider mealtimes and coming and going without a word. Nick, also, had spent the last twelve months without consideration for anyone else. Although happy to have his wife back on his terms, she sometimes felt a nuisance imposing demands, requests and restrictions. She guessed her dark moods couldn't have helped matters. Then, unfortunately, a series of unavoidable incidents threw all of them, especially Carole and Nick, to near breaking point.

The main electricity line down to one of the beach hotels broke and they had no power for seven days while electricians repaired it with a new overhead cable. They lost all their supply of chilled and frozen food and had no means of cooking anyway. For a week, Nick took the children to a nearby hotel for breakfast before taking them to school and himself to work, while house-boy Ali would do the best he could on a purpose built garden fire. The inconvenience was intolerable. No showers, no air conditioning, no refrigerator, no freezer and no cooker. They couldn't even have a straightforward cup of tea. The financial loss was infuriating and with no chilled fresh food, the health risks were enormous.

Just as electricity was finally restored, the storms began. The heaviest deluge they had ever known fell consistently for days, flooding the entire area and making local roads impassable except for four wheel drive vehicles. Nick was still able to get about as usual in his Landrover, but Carole was marooned with her little Mini. Having been under immense strain during the electricity failure, she now sat through the most violent storms she had ever known. The humidity was hundred per cent, and as she watched water trickle constantly through the roof, a musty dampness pervaded the bungalow. Every surface was covered with a thin layer of mould, even Nick's binocular case had fungus growing on it.

After several days, the rains finally stopped leaving everywhere steaming in a sultry heat.

Nick was now impatient to go bird watching having been unable to do so for a while, but Carole was more concerned with two other chores that she wanted him to do. The first was a plumbing problem with inefficient kitchen taps, and for the sake of peace and quiet, he conceded to replace them with new ones. Unfortunately, he was unable to turn off the main water supply, but tried to change them regardless with the predictable result of a flooded kitchen without taps. Attempts to get a plumber left them with a minimum three week wait.

The second job Carole wanted him to do was mend the brakes on her car. Now as impatient as Nick to get out and about, she was hindered by this dangerous mechanical problem on her Mini, but he, like his wife, had had enough of a difficult month and chose to go bird watching. It was an understandable objection on his part, but Carole had been so isolated throughout the last few weeks, the frustration of now being cut off through brake failure rendered her unreasonable, and for the first time, she actually doubted the wisdom of her return at all.

It didn't seem fair. It felt as if she'd battled through cancer, endured a year of unpleasant treatment alone, suffered heartache, misery, sickness and fear, only to return to her family as a loving wife and mother and find no one really cared anyway.

Victoria and Marc did care, Carole knew that really. So did Nick. What did she expect? Perhaps a little recognition, understanding or congratulations might have helped.

One evening, Nick and Carole were sitting quietly in the living room, he was reading and she was sewing, her thoughts reflecting back over the last year as they invariably did. Unintentionally, she sighed out loud.

'What's the matter?' asked Nick, looking over his book.

'I don't know. Nothing really,' Carole shrugged.

'You're always depressed. What's wrong?'

He sounded irritated yet genuinely concerned. She risked an explanation.

'I keep thinking back to all those who are still on St Mary's ward - and the ones who maybe haven't made it. I miss everyone so much, all their care, concern and friendship. I feel almost guilty being here away from it all, yet so isolated.'

'It's time to put all that behind you and get on with living,' Nick said.

'I know. But I can't. I wish you could understand.'

Nick shook his head despairingly, then buried his nose back in his book. Subject closed.

The next day Carole bought a postcard and sent it to everyone on St Mary's ward, wondering if they would remember her and wondering if Dr Khanna would read it. If Dr Khanna had known what she had come back to, he would never have let her come, she mused. The health risks from no refrigeration followed by hundred per cent humidity, torrential storms and overwhelming stress had certainly been a baptism of fire rather than the easy, loving transition she'd anticipated!

And now, another anxiety had started to eat itself into her thoughts.

Did Hodgkin's Disease come back? Was she cured, or in 'remission', whatever that meant? Did she only have borrowed time? Carole realized that she still didn't know anything and suddenly felt vulnerable and frightened. She had been so preoccupied with getting the treatment behind her, she'd almost lost sight of what it had all been for. Having succeeded in completing that, her thoughts then had been concerned with Tanzania, being back with Nick and the children. It hadn't really occurred to her before that she was anything other than cured, but no-one had said that it would never return.

The first of Carole's two monthly blood tests and examination with her doctor in Dar es Salaam loomed near, and what might that reveal?

CHAPTER FOURTEEN

Will the Real Carole Baker Now Stand Up

Nothing had prepared Carole for the absolute horror of Tanzanian medical practice. The psychological trauma in being subjected to familiar blood tests again was overwhelming, but that turned to sheer panic when she saw the basic laboratory conditions.

A crude surgery with just an examination couch, sink and chair provided full amenities for her check up. If Nick hadn't been with her, she may well have walked out on the spot - Dr Khanna would have been horrified. Fears over the shabby lack of hygiene mingled with a flooded mass of memories, but, Carole was relieved to observe, the needle was obviously sterile.

'How would I know if Hodgkin's Disease returned?' Carole asked the doctor, who did actually seem most kind and efficient.

'Well, the blood test would probably show an increase in lymphocytes or, as far as you're concerned, the discovery of another lump.'

She didn't understand about the lymphocytes but felt comforted that the doctor had obliged her with an answer. Moreover, he was prepared to let Carole have a copy of the test results as soon as they were ready. For the first time, facing the truth seemed a more reassuring alternative than avoidance and as soon as she received them, she wrote a detailed copy to Marianne and her husband Pete begging for any researched information.

The doctor had told her everything remained clear, and a speedy reply from Pete and Marianne who laboriously tooth-combed the medical section of the reference library confirmed that her monocytes, basophiles, platelets, neutrophils, WBC, HB and ESR appeared to be in order - though in truth none of them knew what they were on about!

It seemed that from a physical point of view, Carole was making steady progress but from an emotional aspect, she was still plagued with bouts of depression and loneliness. If she was to be honest with herself, the return back to her family was proving a let down. Victoria and Marc had matured into young independent individuals who bore the resilience of twelve month's neglect. They were fun company, but were still adjusting to their mother's rather demanding presence. With Nick, the problem was more serious. After a brief surge of passion, the relationship had cooled into detached indifference, at least, on his part. They couldn't reach each other and the more Carole tried to scratch and claw for response, the further he pulled away.

Maybe things would improve in time. For now, it served to deepen Carole's depression adding embittered feelings of resentment and injustice. She had fought cancer as much for Nick's sake as hers; she'd had every right to divorce him on the grounds of his past infidelity with Lynn, but had stayed by him for their future together as a family. Carole's battle with Hodgkin's Disease and the treatment, plus her loyalty, seemed a contribution worthy of his total love and affection in return. She wasn't getting it and it didn't feel fair. And she didn't have the strength to fight another battle or put up with more upheaval. It seemed Carole had no option now but to resign herself to whatever life threw at her.

A trip to England grew imminent for her second check up with Dr Khanna in July. Carole would stay for a month, taking Victoria and Marc with her, with Nick joining them for the last two weeks before they all travelled back together. It was an important journey in more ways than one. She was longing to see her parents, visit St Mary's ward, even Dr Khanna - but most especially to talk with Eunice.

The jet touched down at Heathrow at six o'clock on Friday July 20th 1984 to a cold, bleak British summer's morning. Despite the inclement weather, Carole was overjoyed to be back in England. Mum and dad were there to meet them, and as dad drove up the motorway, Carole and her mum nattered incessantly above the noisy laughter of Victoria and Marc's made up travel games.

Carole felt so happy!

But she'd felt so happy just four months ago arriving in Dar es Salaam. That had barely lasted ten days. Happiness could be very fragile - and right then, she held on to it tightly.

'Oh, Eunice,' Carole whimpered, curled up on the settee in her friend's living room the next evening. 'I just feel so unwanted there - yet what can I do?'

'You could always come back here, to England.'

'But I can't! I would be leaving everything behind. The children are so happy there, they have their own busy lives and would never want to come back to England. I couldn't bear to be separated from them again. And Pinky - I can't leave her. I feel so trapped, so tired of struggling. And I'm scared that all my worrying and sadness will bring the cancer back.'

Eunice listened patiently while Carole moaned on and on. Oh, what a relief to have such a good moan! Eventually, Eunice drew in a deep breath.

'Remember,' she said with quiet authority, 'it's *your* life. You owe it to yourself to choose to do whatever you want. You have not conquered cancer for Nick's benefit - or anyone else's for that matter. You've fought it for *you*, and you're hundred per cent successful on that score.'

She leaned back assertively in the chair. There was more to come.

'You're only as trapped as you let yourself be. After everything you've been through you've proved how strong you are. There is absolutely nothing to stop you rebuilding your life - whatever way you want it - either here or there. It's not just a question of what people, or family, are doing to you; it's your reaction to it that needs to be looked at. You say you are trapped, you could just as easily say you're as free as a bird. What's stopping you just going on out there and doing your own thing? Remember, keep your priorities right - that's with yourself, number one.'

There was more.

It wasn't really a reprimand, but it stopped Carole in her tracks of self pity and was just what she needed. She slept soundly that night. Tiredness from the long journey had caught up with her to merge with the spent release of emotion and shared troubles. But all through her dreams and even on waking she was haunted by Eunice's words. 'You're only as trapped as you let yourself be, you could just as easily say you're as free as a bird.' Maybe she hadn't conquered cancer just for Nick's benefit. Carole had always thought of herself as half a partnership, a quarter of the family - never just as herself. Somehow she'd imagined that her sole purpose for survival had been to return to Dar es Salaam as a loving wife and mother... but perhaps instead of being this wife and mother that nobody wanted, she ought to think about being Carole. Perhaps it was time to realize she had fought this disease for *herself.*

What a triumphant thought! Suddenly all the negative aspects were overridden by a wonderful surge of optimism. For the first time since the end of treatment, or maybe since her illness had been diagnosed, she felt a positive energy of independence, determination and challenge that she had never experienced in her life before.

However, all the revolutionary philosophising didn't bear much credence as Carole's appointment with Dr Khanna approached. Weak and vulnerable once again, she dragged poor Eunice along with her for moral support.

There was a full body scan complete with aniseed refreshment, followed by a lengthy examination, blood tests and interrogation by Dr Khanna. Carole maintained a discreet silence over too many details, reassuring him of good overall health in ideal conditions. She would have to wait a couple of days for the results from the blood tests, but it was obvious that Dr Khanna was happy.

'I think we can feel satisfied that all is in order, Mrs Baker. As soon as the final results confirm this, I shall want you to make an appointment to see me in November.'

Dear God, what wonderful words! Of course, Carole would have to visit her doctor in Tanzania in eight weeks, but in some ways, these regular examinations were reassuring. Rejoining Eunice, Carole smiled with relief.

'Oh Eunice, I must go and have a chat with the nurses in St Mary's ward!'

As they both headed off in that direction, Carole realized this was no ghost to lay. The memory was poignantly fresh and alive; the treatment may have been behind her but there remained still a tentative link. As soon as she walked through the swing doors onto the ward, the memory came flooding back as if it had been yesterday. Immediately, two of the nurses on duty greeted their old patient with delight.

'Hello!' they chorused, 'Oh, you look great!'

Carole and Eunice chatted with them for several minutes, swapping stories of their events on St Mary's ward with hers of Africa. Then, remembering the Friday morning chemotherapy friends, Carole eventually asked after them, wanting to know yet hesitant to hear.

Two had died.

But there again, that meant several of them were still soldiering on. Carole's eyes glanced down the length of the ward; still the same postcards on the wall, the same screens, the same curtains, the same smell... a few beds had patients in them - many were empty, waiting for the chemotherapy weekenders.

Suddenly she felt she'd had enough.

'Come on, Eunice. It's time we went now.'

Preoccupied now with their own thoughts, Eunice and Carole walked silently back to the car and home.

The remaining two weeks served to fuel a new found sense of optimism in Carole aided by an unexpected blistering heatwave. While Victoria and Marc enjoyed sunbathing in the back garden, Carole delighted in a hectic round of meals, drinks and shopping with friends and family - marred only by reserved feelings of Nick's imminent arrival.

But something had changed.

A spark of confidence ignited by Eunice had grown to provide a glow of newly discovered independence within her. Now she realized she had choices, control, power over her own life. She had no obligation or commitment or duty to anyone but herself. It was a precious revelation but quite what to do about it was still rather vague!

The night before Nick was due to arrive, Carole stood alone in the bedroom staring at her reflection in the mirror. Suddenly, laughing out loud, she winked at her image then, with a broad, mischievous grin, proclaimed,

'Will the real Carole Baker now stand up please!'

CHAPTER FIFTEEN

The Final Blow

In the bedroom back at Enderby, Carole and Nick were packing their suitcases in preparation for travelling back to Dar es Salaam. His joining them in Leicester had actually been quite enjoyable but as Carole's eyes now suddenly caught sight of the old tell tale stains of trifle from her Christmas outburst, she was reminded of that past anger.

'Do you still have anything going with Lynn?' Carole heard herself asking.

Nick was visibly unnerved by the unprovoked interrogation, compressing the half filled contents of his suitcase with unnecessary vigour.

'No', he answered slowly, 'I rarely see or hear anything of her anymore.'

Studying his face, Carole searched for deceit. He looked thinner these days and older. Years in the hot dry African climate had weathered his skin but he looked good - thought right now decidedly uneasy. Maybe he had noticed the stain on the wall, too.

It was important for her to know the truth. She had decided to give their marriage until November, the month she was due back in England again for tests, and if things hadn't improved by then she would consider returning permanently. Carole wanted it to work, she wanted to stay in Tanzania, but she was no longer prepared to sacrifice her future in holding onto an empty relationship. She believed Lynn to be a whim of the past, yet she still understood they had to make allowances and adjustments to stay happy together.

One thing that had changed though, was that at last Carole felt able to cope - whatever happened. The realization of her own control gave her a safe feeling, and in a strange way, she was beginning to be proud of having had cancer. After all, it was basically this experience which was so constructive in her own personal growth, plus a bit of help from Eunice!

It was the first time in years that the four of them had travelled together without leaving one or the other behind, and the journey back was welcomed by Carole as a positive challenge just to see how everything evolved over the next four months.

Back home in Dar es Salaam, Carole's previous bouts of depression were becoming less frequent. Although to some extent, a new independence was carrying her forward, she had since learned that post cancer depression was a common occurrence anyway, a normal response to trauma. She could have done with knowing that six months ago.

Nick and Carole were plodding along quite comfortably. She had 'let go' of demands and expectations and this had released much of the tension between them. The children were aware of a happier atmosphere and the house was once again filled with laughter. Aware that Victoria and Marc no longer needed their mother as they once had, she adapted now to enjoying their young adult company. They both had a great sense of fun and all of them teased each other relentlessly. Victoria was approaching her fifteenth birthday and her blossoming maturity revealed a sensitive, caring confidence blended with lively humour. Carole was so proud of them. Life was good. Strangely enough, letting go of working at her marriage had made everyone so much more comfortable, it was beginning to look as if she might stay.

Jean, her ex-colleague from the High Commission where Carole used to work, was having a few problems of her own. She came round for coffee one morning to off load her troubles.

'Why don't we give ourselves a holiday?' Carole suggested spontaneously.

'Oh, I could just do with that,' she admitted, 'away from husbands - imagine!' The desperate look in her eyes fuelled Carole's determination.

'Right. We *will* have a holiday, never mind what the men say!'

The next fifteen minutes were spent excitedly planning a route, calculating costs and deciding dates. The result was Zimbabwe by Air Tanzania for a week in the middle of October - six weeks ahead. If they started saving now, they could afford a good hotel, splendid food and wine, a trip to Victoria Falls - with enough left over for fun! Nick was not pleased with this exclusive female break but sensed their determination and sulkily left them to get on with it. But first of all, two other events loomed near. The first, an imminent blood test and the second, Victoria's birthday on 20th September, just ten days ahead. Perhaps this meant so much to Carole because of memories from the previous year when she'd lain ill in the Leicester Royal Infirmary. It had seemed then that she might not be around for her daughter's next birthday, let alone feeling well enough to plan a trip to Zimbabwe! Time changes things so much, she now reflected and wondered idly where she might be this time the following year - for Victoria's sixteenth birthday.

The blood test and examination revealed all was still well. Carole certainly felt much better than she had for ages and she certainly looked after herself with conscientious care. Psychologically she was much stronger, too.

Unfortunately, Nick was scheduled to be away on a business trip in Nairobi for Victoria's birthday, but maybe the celebration was more a private triumph for Carole alone anyway. She woke her daughter early that morning, rudely singing 'Happy Birthday!' while Victoria sleepily protested, pulling the cool, cotton sheet ineffectually over her ears.

Fifteen years old, Carole thought, her mind slipping back to when she'd been that age - already seriously involved with Nick. Looking at her daughter now, peeping mischievously over the bedcover, so pretty, so youthful, so sweet, it seemed far too young an age to seal a destiny and sign away a life.

Of course, it hadn't really been like that. It had been her own choice as much as everyone else's. Hadn't it? Or maybe, she reflected soberly, she was only just learning now to separate and recognize her choices from those of others. By the time Carole was seventeen, she'd been pregnant with Victoria and she and Nick had been expected to marry. Carole grinned at Victoria. She guessed she had been worth it and maybe they hadn't done so badly after all!

After breakfast, Carole drove the children to school and collected the mail from the post office. There must have been about twenty cards for Victoria and she carefully laid them out on the table for her daughter to open when she came home. The only other letter was addressed to Nick. She recognized the handwriting, it was from a friend of his called Sam whom she actively disliked. A condescending, arrogant man. Fortunately, distance inhibited too much contact but even his occasional correspondence with Nick made Nick secretive, furtive - and Carole suspicious. She placed the envelope on a shelf for Nick's return in a few day's time. Then she took it down and held it up to the light, trying to decipher any words through the envelope. But she couldn't read a thing.

Throughout the day, that letter haunted her. She even toyed with the idea of steaming it open. Carole wasn't usually obsessed with the thought of reading Nick's mail but for some reason, the opportunity tormented her.

'I don't know, Pinky,' she confessed to her loyal companion, 'whatever's got into me?' Carole was now in the throes of baking bread, but squatted down to caress Pinky's ears. 'It's only a silly old letter from Sam'. As she stood up and dusted her hands on the apron, she laughed to see Pinky, her ears covered in white flour. Pinky seemed to laugh back, then bounded up, tail wagging as she heard the children arrive back home from school. Victoria immediately began to tear open her birthday cards while Marc delved into cupboards hunting frantically for morsels of food. The bread was now left to prove so Carole set the table for tea - complete with home baked birthday cake. Pinky became far more interested in the children than their mum and as they sat down to eat, Carole went into the kitchen, impulsively took the letter down from the shelf and opened it.

And paid the price.

'...Have you managed another one of your dirty weekends with Lynn again recently?'

The words just pounced at her. Desperately she tried to keep control, readjust her understanding of what she'd read, but the room started spinning, her heart raced and her throat went dry. It was quite clear what she'd read.

Victoria came in for something and saw her mother standing there, chalk white, shaking and holding onto the table.

'Mum, are you all right?'

Carole looked at her. The birthday girl. Oh, what could she say? Tears started to roll down her cheeks, the whole impact of those words meant, quite simply, that their marriage was over. That was it. Where was her strength now? She had to go. Poor Victoria. Poor Marc. Poor Carole.

'Put the kettle on, Victoria,' she wept softly, 'and go and fetch Marc. We need to have a little family chat, the three of us.'

Victoria's face drained of colour. She immediately called Marc and busied herself around the kettle. Marc came in and straight away picked up the tension. Carole's heart felt leaden. She knew now she was going to go and live in England. Alone. She was about to lose her whole family - even Pinky.

They all sat down with their cups of tea. Carole took a deep breath and started to explain everything.

'Before I was ill, your dad told me he had fallen in love with Lynn. In fact it was my sadness that probably made me ill in the first place.' Carole read them the contents of Sam's letter which made it very clear the affair was, and always had been, an ongoing relationship. 'It seems he still loves her. I don't think I can stay any longer. I'm frightened it will make me ill again - I've not really been happy since I came back but now it's definitely time for me to go.'

She sat back, hurting and scared, and waited for their reaction. At first there was nothing but blank stares. Open mouthed, they looked at their mother in vacant disbelief, then slowly the truth began to register.

'We want to stay with you, mum!' Victoria exploded.

'I want to live in England, with you,' echoed Marc soberly.

The sweetest compensation Carole had never for one moment imagined came in absolute unison from their lips. In unfaltering loyalty they were instantly prepared to cut off their lives, sever friendships, leave a country they loved, to stay with their mum. Their totally unexpected allegiance unleashed a torrent of tension and Carole completely broke down. Victoria rushed over, putting her arm around her.

'Oh mum, it'll be okay. Don't cry.'

'I'm so sorry,' Carole wept, 'and on your birthday, too. I didn't want it to be like this.'

Pinky lay motionless at Marc's feet, looking up at everyone for reassurance while her flattened ears were massaged by Marc's nervous hands.

'Lynn. Yuk,' he muttered disapprovingly.

'Tell me,' Carole said quietly, 'did you two often go to Mufindi with dad?'

'Yes,' they both admitted, 'but we didn't think...'

Fool.

What a fool she'd been. It had never ever ended. He was probably with her right now in Nairobi.

'When will we be going back?' asked Marc eventually.

'At the end of your school term in June next year.' It was all falling into place. 'I shall go back in November for my blood test and while I'm there I'll let everyone know and set things in motion.'

'God, I *hate* him!' Victoria suddenly erupted.

Marc's jaw was set in barely controlled aggression. He looked so like his father at times, and now, in simmering temper, his youthful age belied the adult turmoil churning within him. They were both so angry with their father that whilst Carole secretly valued their support, she had to be careful not to inadvertently feed contempt. Now it was her turn to offer comfort.

'We'll be fine, you'll see.'

Pinky still lay at Marc's feet, unmoving except for her large, frightened eyes searching desperately between them for security, ears flat to her head, tail down. Something very bad was happening.

Victoria was the first to say it.

'But what about Pinky?'

Carole looked at them both in turn, then cast her eyes down on the dog. Softly remembering a promise she had made to her in her darkest hours, she smiled back up at the children.

'Pinky will come to England, too. Yes. Pinky will come too.'

CHAPTER SIXTEEN

A Verbal Vendetta

'What on earth have you told them for?' snapped Nick.

No longer did Carole care how annoyed Nick might be with her for opening his mail, the contents overrode any argument for privacy, but it seemed Nick was more angry that she had exposed his infidelity to the children.

'I needed to know exactly how they felt. They have a part in all this, you know.' And Carole proceeded to tell him of their plans to return to England. Nick had the audacity to feel most upset and it was with great relief that she shortly escaped with Jean to Zimbabwe.

October is recognized as the hottest month in Zimbabwe, the end of the dry season, but the air remains clean and fresh throughout. To the west, the huge, flat game reserve at Wankie blends in dramatic contrast with the mountainous region of the eastern border, but it was the area at Victoria Falls in the north, boasting the world's second greatest waterfall, where they had planned to stay. Neither Carole nor Jean had been to the area before and they were both overwhelmed with the breathtaking sight of the Zambezi River plunging down the mile-long arc of Victoria Falls, the roaring torrent providing a natural backcloth for sleeping crocodiles and roaming elephants. They went on to enjoy a week visiting local African villages, watching displays of tribal dancing and visiting witch doctors, while the evenings were squandered away gambling blackjack and roulette in a nearby casino. On the last evening, she and Jean took a memorable river trip and 'sundowner' on the Zambezi River with a final indulgence of first class cuisine at a plush hotel. There, they toasted their chilled wine to one of the happiest holidays of their lives.

They returned back renewed, refreshed and ready to tackle anything, which, under the circumstances, was probably a good thing. The children and Pinky were delighted to have their mother back, but Nick barely acknowledged her presence. It reaffirmed Carole's decision to go - and the sooner the better. But not before seizing a timely opportunity to enjoy some sweet revenge.

Victoria, a friend and Carole had planned a shopping trip in town. Carole had a domestic message she wanted to leave with Nick, so they drove by his office en route. He wasn't there so Carole decided to scribble him a note. But then she noticed a telex had just arrived, as yet unread. She picked it up.

'Visiting Brook Bond Beach House. Call over to see me as soon as you can, all my love - Lynn.'

Disregarding her own message, Carole crunched the telex into a ball and stormed out of the office.

'What on earth's the matter, mum?' asked Victoria, visibly unnerved by her mum's temper. Carole told her.

'Why don't you go over to the Beach House yourself,' they both suggested, 'and get a few things off your chest?'

Mmm, why not? They all planned to meet couple of hours later in town and Carole got back into her car and drove with tight lipped determination to Brook Bond Beach House.

It was an old colonial building for private use and converted to sleep fifteen to twenty people. There was invariably a house full staying, people either flying in or out or maybe using it as a weekend retreat. Carole pulled up and knocked on the door. A woman she recognized to be Lynn's mother answered and Carole asked to speak to her daughter.

'She's in the bathroom...' she said. Lynn could be heard in the background asking who it was. Before Lynn's mother had time to answer, Lynn herself came to the door and they stood there face to face. Immediately, she stiffened but forced a false smile.

'Hello?' she offered cautiously.

'Lynn, I think you and I have got a few things to talk about, don't you?' Carole's heart pounded fit to burst, yet her mind remained controlled, cool and crystal clear.

'I'll come to the car with you.'

Lynn's mother looked at them both, sensing it best to stay silent and Carole wondered if she knew. As soon as Lynn had sat in the passenger seat, Carole drove a short distance up the road to a discreet, secluded area, parked up, took a deep breath and stared straight at her. She then gave vent to a full, fifteen minute verbal vendetta, lecturing her on moral ethics, values, love and loyalty, on her cruel destruction of two marriages, of breaking up two families; she accused her of behaving inhumanely under Carole's own tragic circumstances and hurled an attack of aggressive pent up anger.

Lynn just sat there.

'It's not just me...' she meekly protested.

But Carole didn't care what she said. She wasn't bothered whether or not she was justified with her anger. She just wanted to off load over two years of anguish onto her, dump over two years of blame squarely on her shoulders - irrespective of the fairness of it all. Had she received fair treatment? So far, through 1982, 1983 and 1984 Lynn had escaped any confrontation with her. In fact Carole had avoided any. But now she felt stronger and more able to take control and here was an opportunity to give vent. It was hardly a time to proportion blame fairly. Carole's marriage was over. She had nothing more to lose - so she gave her the lot.

Finally, Carole simmered to an empty end. Sensing she had finished, Lynn opened the car door and slunk away like a scolded cat. Carole's heart was no longer racing with the surge of vengeful adrenaline - but pounded softly with a quiet, spent yet satisfied exhaustion, like a soloist who'd just achieved his ultimate performance.

Maybe all that had done no good. What good could have been done anyway? She knew really that she had to cut off all bitterness, shed negative remorse and go forward with hope. But just for that moment, Carole tasted the bitter sweet flavour of perverse justice. The balance had somehow been redressed and it felt great!!

She sat up straight in the car, tossed back her hair in a gesture of triumph, turned on the ignition - and, as she looked in the mirror before driving away, was momentarily startled by her own reflection. The flashing eyes of a confident young woman ablaze with vigour and determination stared back at her. Smiling at her own strengthened image, she acknowledged that no way would she have confronted Lynn like that a year ago. In fact, there was no way she would have had the courage to take a holiday in Zimbabwe without Nick a year ago. There was no way she would have dared contemplate moving back to England on her own a year ago. Strange, Carole thought, how courage could release feelings of helplessness or of being trapped - as if timidity was a prison for the soul.

A comfortable sense of calm settled over her, a feeling of being in control and believing in herself. She knew she could cope. The future was now something for her to shape, mould, steer and develop - not just a blank destiny waiting for events to happen. Of course, there would be times when fate would deliver problems, but she would always be able to solve them.

For the first time ever, the future showed itself as a challenge - with hope. Carole felt pleased with herself. She liked herself. As if a small light glowed in the distance, Carole saw a new tomorrow and she remembered something Eunice had once said to her.

'What's stopping you just going on out there and doing your own thing?'

Mmm. Quite.

CHAPTER SEVENTEEN

The Wheels in Motion

Carole's next flight to England was booked for November 26th 1984. Although this was primarily for her appointment with Dr Khanna it offered an ideal opportunity to initiate the first steps for returning permanently.

She planned to tell both her parents and Nick's that she and Nick were breaking up and she knew she had to sort out some temporary housing arrangement. Poor mum and dad had had their lives turned upside down during the last few years; was she now going to be forced to ask for their help yet again? With Marc and Victoria, her parents wouldn't want to put them up for long - but where else could they stay? She would need to buy a house. But Carole had no more idea of how to buy a house than fly. Also, there were innumerable problems to work through ranging from how to bring Pinky to England to learning financial independence - let alone coping with the emotional stress of starting anew. Also it was a daunting prospect being single again at thirty-two and she had to battle occasionally with the lazier option of just putting up with everything and staying.

But if paving the way for a new life in England seemed an ordeal, the imminent journey did not. A local friend had won first prize in a competition - the prize being a return air ticket from Dar es Salaam to London, Club Class. Carole had eagerly bought this ticket from her at a much reduced price, giving her friend considerable ready cash and Carole the privilege of luxury travel. They were both delighted with the exchange.

On the day of her flight, Carole boarded the plane and was immediately ushered to a plush seat with a waiting glass of champagne. Throughout the journey she was treated as a VIP with a steward close by offering individual attention at all times to ensure the ultimate in comfort. To add to her enjoyment, as they flew over Cairo the pilot had to circle several times for clearance and took the opportunity of pointing out to the passengers specific landmarks of Cairo and the Pyramids. In all, the flight was probably the best she had ever had and put her in excellent form for taking on the next two weeks.

On Monday 3rd December, Carole had her appointment with Dr Khanna at the Leicester Royal Infirmary. She was saying nothing to her parents until this was out of the way, although she did mention it to the doctor. Happily, blood tests and examination revealed everything remained clear with a following appointment due for April 1985. But as Carole was now planning to return permanently in June, she asked Dr Khanna if she could delay the next examination by one month. In fact not only was he happy to postpone the date, he suggested they leave it until July - thus completing the first year of post-treatment care, and earning extended time between follow-up appointments. She would have to continue with regular checks for about eight years, but at least every positive result promised greater assurance of a permanent cure.

The next day, after dinner, Carole and her mum and dad sat idly talking about the future. It was the ideal time to tell them but she felt suddenly nervous and anxious.

'Actually, I may be coming back...' she said, suddenly aware of her parents' eyes focused on their daughter. 'Permanently. I think Nick and I are going to split up.'

There. It was out.

Carole's parents listened now intently with sad concern as she told them all about Lynn, the struggles, the battle to carry on and the final defeat. Strangely, they were not particularly surprised. Mum in particular had sensed things were not right and their support was immediate. Of course they could come back to Enderby and stay as long as they needed to.

It was such a relief to have unburdened her problems onto them and make the impending separation 'official' as it were. Now she had to tell Nick's parents.

'Hello, it's me,' Carole said to Nick's mum on the phone later that day.

'Hello love! How are you?'

'Oh, okay... look, can I come and have a chat with you?'

'Of course you can, love, come straight round. I'll put the kettle on.'

Living only a few minutes walk away from her parents' house in Enderby, she was there within a quarter of an hour. Unlike her own mum and dad, they had absolutely no idea there was anything wrong with her marriage and were devastated. And furious with Nick. Throwing her hands up in despair, Nick's mother fumed at her son's infidelity and vowed full support for Carole and the children. Nick's father remained tight lipped but nodded affirmation with his wife's every remark.

Carole was so relieved to have it all out in the open and doubly relieved to have such support. She hadn't protected Nick but nor had she exaggerated the situation to earn sympathy. It was a case of survival and she needed all the help she could find. But now Carole wanted to simply enjoy the rest of her stay in Leicestershire visiting friends and shopping.

It was typical English December weather; cold, damp and grey. In Dar es Salaam right now the climate was hot and dry. Undoubtedly, Marc and Victoria would be enjoying the local beach, their toasted brown limbs swimming, sunbathing and sailing under the scorching African sun. Carole's thoughts drifted back to their magnificent home, the colourful tropical wildlife, the African land that she loved, the beautiful Tanzanian coastline, her friends, a houseboy always at hand, all their dogs and cats - but if it hurt her, how much would it hurt the children?

Nevertheless, Carole enjoyed the remaining two weeks in England, psychologically preparing herself for coming back and insisting that Eunice and Joy visit her for a fortnight's safari holiday in Africa while the opportunity still existed. They readily agreed knowing time was at a premium and tentatively planned to travel over for Easter, four months away.

In all, Carole had accomplished as much as she had expected and wanted to. It was time to go back, but strange realizing the next time she stood on British soil it would be forever.

Her Club Class return flight was as comfortable as before with the additional pleasure of attractive male company. They chatted comfortably together, their minds too active for sleep, talking into the early hours of the morning. Carole felt flattered by his attention, and further enjoyed more fuss when a male steward joined them, joking that as there were no children on board, would she like to accept the pilots' invitation to visit the flight deck. She eagerly accepted the offer and was fascinated at the spectacular view from the cockpit where the twinkling lights of Luxor lit up the black sky like fairy lights. The captain cheerfully tried to explain some of the operational procedures of flying the plane but this was way beyond her understanding. She was much more confident when they talked about Tanzania. Some twenty minutes later Carole returned to her handsome male companion feeling thoroughly privileged and honoured. His charm continued to please her and in all, the whole journey boosted her ego.

It needed boosting.

She was going to be single again.

On her return, Carole found Nick was away in Uganda with Sam attending an ornithological conference. It was unbelievably hot and confusing to exchange thoughts of a white Christmas for a tropical one. Victoria, looking bronzed and beautiful, laughingly confessed she was going to enter the 1985 Dar es Salaam Yacht Club beauty competition, 'for a joke' as she put it, and Marc informed his mum that Kizzy was pregnant again.

Four days later Nick arrived back.

'God, I was so scared you wouldn't be here,' he admitted, holding her tightly.

His warmth unnerved her. It shocked him too that his wife's presence suddenly mattered so much to him. It threw them both into turmoil. In fact, the following two weeks were completely and unexpectedly happy; laughing and loving in a way long since forgotten. Carole literally didn't know whether she was coming or going.

On December 15th, a long awaited delivery of goods arrived from England to include a new L.W.B. County Landrover ordered from Leicester six months previously, plus a shipment of domestic items Carole had bought on recent UK trips. Victoria and Marc joined them as they off loaded and unwrapped hundreds of rolls of toilet tissue, shampoo, flour, packet mixes, chocolate, toothpaste - not to mention the thrill of the Landrover itself! Pinky watched them, tail wagging optimistically. She was not to be disappointed.

'Catch Pinky!' laughed Marc, throwing a large leather bone high into the blue sky.

The weekend before Christmas, impatient to try the new vehicle, they planned a short camping break at the Mikumi National Park with some local friends. It had been driving through this reserve that Nick had first said those words 'I think I love her' so long ago.

Despite the poignant reminder and disregarding her plans to end the marriage, Carole somehow blocked off future problems to simply live for the day. Eight of them piled into the Landrover, the four of them with friends who knew nothing about her decision to leave Nick, and they all thoroughly enjoyed four days in the baking sun watching lions, leopards and other big game. They returned back to prepare for Christmas celebrations in good humour. The shipped container of goods provided them with plenty of food and drink and on Christmas Day they enjoyed a traditional dinner with roast turkey, stuffing and all the trimmings.

It was exactly a year ago Carole had thrown the trifle full pelt into Nick's face. Watching him now, content, full, surrounded by his family and animals, she knew he loved them all, loved her - but he loved another woman too. Perhaps he would have liked to keep them all. However, Carole's philosophising was soon curtailed by the sudden restless activity of Kizzy. She was about to produce pups! The prepared whelping box was rejected at the eleventh hour in preference for the wardrobe, and there, she gave birth to eight adorable little bundles.

The seasonal festivities continued with a hectic round of parties amongst their close circle of friends, finishing off with a New Years' Eve party at the Yacht Club where Victoria learned she had won first prize as Miss Dar es Salaam in the Yacht Club competition! This entitled her to a free helicopter ride, a radio cassette, clock and pendant, not to mention the prestige of it all.

The evening of December 31st 1984 was mild; the club house was situated on the beach and Carole felt intoxicated with the beauty of their surroundings as much as from the free flowing wine. Music and laughter mingled with the soft sound of the sea, it's calm blackness twinkling as it caught the reflection of the club's fairy lights. At midnight, chimes from the club house clock announced the start of a New Year. Carole could hear everyone cheering, but she and Nick were drawn into their own emotions. Slowly, he pulled her to him. His body felt good, familiar, warm. She wanted him. She was confused. His eyes searched hers. Tenderly, they kissed New Years' Eve.

'Oh, Nick - will this be our last together?'

'Of course not,' he promised.

CHAPTER EIGHTEEN

See You Soon, Pinky

It was crazy. Carole felt so confused and unsettled. They both did. It had taken so long for her to make the decision for them to separate, and now this.

Did they still love each other enough for it to work?

But any hesitation on her part was short lived; her suspicious mind ruined it all the next day when she sneakily nosed through his briefcase innocently left open in their bedroom. There was a letter Nick had written to Lynn telling her about the recent conference he had attended, and for some reason not posted. Although the contents spoke of little other than birds - there were even some sample feathers enclosed - Carole must have been suffering from a hair trigger jealousy syndrome. In a blind rage of fury, she screamed into the living room, shattering the peace and quiet for Nick, Marc and Victoria, and waved the letter around in a verbal explosion of obscenities. The children were visibly scared of her. Where was their mother's control? Had she gone mad? Nick's jaw clenched and the colour drained from his face, but more in anger than guilt. Firmly but gently he led his wife into their bedroom, sat her on the bed and tried to console her. But his patience was stretched to the limit and his manner was stern. Undoubtedly she had just ruined any chance of reconciliation, but it was also obvious she had no trust left in him anymore either.

Worse was to follow.

A week later, Carole called by at his office to deliver a message. She was told he wasn't there but would be back in about ten minutes. Immediately then gripped by a furtive opportunity to search, Carole smiled her way into his office on the pretext of leaving a note on his desk. Once in, she quickly opened first the top drawer - nothing of interest to her there. Then the middle drawer - again, nothing. But there, in the bottom drawer, she found what she was dreading and yet looking for. Several thick bundles of personal letters from Lynn, collected through the years and neatly tied in date order. Carole pulled them out, opened one, read it and tore it to shreds letting the bits of paper litter his office floor. Then she opened another, ripped it to shreds, and another, and another.

Nick walked in and froze.

The floor was a white carpet of shredded paper. She carried on regardless, staring at him, her eyes full of hatred.

'Can't you mind your own business?' he spat through gritted teeth.

'It *is* my business!' screamed Carole, turning now on her heels and out of his office, leaving him there, angry and humiliated amongst the tattered torn shreds of his exposed infidelity.

The incident was never again referred to. They just slipped straight back into icy detachment. Nick felt he had no privacy left; it was as if Carole had upturned every stone, revealing all its underlying filth, deceit and lies. There was nothing left to hide and nowhere to hide it anyway. The peculiar thing was her own quickening ability to pick herself up, dust herself down and get on with other more important things.

And high on her agenda was learning to swim. Fear of water, or at any rate, fear of taking her feet off the bottom, had always inhibited Carole learning to swim but now she decided to enrol for lessons at the local school's private pool with a trained instructor. A more important achievement for her than it looked.

It was strange, the subtle changes that were evolving in her character. Carole remembered something she'd read once about a 'cancer personality' - that those prone to suppressing emotions or harbouring grief were supposedly more likely to succumb to cancer than the positive, outspoken optimist. There was probably no truth in it - but she was certainly now intent on guarding her future!

Poor Kizzy's future was also safeguarded - from having any further litters! In Dar es Salaam in the mid-eighties, there was no veterinary centre that offered surgery, and so one Saturday, the local vet visited to perform poor Kizzy's spaying on the dining room table at home. He left immediately after with brief instructions on how to administer the necessary follow-on antibiotic injections and post operative care.

Perhaps it was just as well she *had* returned to England for her own treatment, she now reflected thoughtfully.

Easter came, bringing Eunice and Joy to Dar es Salaam for a last opportune safari holiday in Kenya. Nick was away on business in Botswana when they arrived and wasn't expected to return before they left, but it was a delight for Carole to welcome them into her home. After a couple of days relaxing, they started the first leg of their travels, boarding a flight to Arusha in northern Tanzania where they were met by their African guide and his Landrover. He drove them to their first stopover, the Lake Manyara

Hotel, perched precariously on the very edge of the Great Rift Valley with spectacular views falling away beneath. Behind them stood the majestic peak of Mount Meru, and before them, steeply forested slopes tumbled into the vast shimmering lake Manyara. The scenery overwhelmed the three of them, but their aesthetic enlightenment was crudely shortlived. Joy retired to bed early, leaving Carole and Eunice drinking and talking together in the hotel bar when they were unexpectedly joined by a bronzed, blond Scandinavian male.

'Excuse me ladies,' he said politely in broken English, 'but I would very much like to take you two young ladies to bed.'

Eunice and Carole just looked at each other, unsure if what they'd really heard was true, then rejected their lustful admirer with polite but immediate dismissal. He left apologetically while the two of them gaped at one another before spluttering over their wine in a heap of giggles. Nevertheless, they took note that as unaccompanied females they needed to be careful.

The following morning as the three of them made their way to breakfast, Eunice noticed what she thought to be a gimmicky tourist attraction.

'Look at those stuffed baboons perched on those logs! Don't they look real!'

'They *are* real,' laughed Carole, enjoying their pleasure at finding unexpected wildlife before they had even begun their safari.

After a light meal, their guide drove the three of them into the Serengeti to Lake Ndutu camp. The journey took them through rough, parched terrain, flat and dry with herds of bedraggled, scrawny hyenas scattering as they noisily bounced over the dusty track. The campsite provided them with very basic amenities but as this was just an overnight stop before venturing further into the Serengeti up to the Olduvai Gorge, it was perfectly acceptable. Rare sounds echoed through the night, but they slept surprisingly well and welcomed the next day with much anticipation.

Journeying on, the Serengeti sprawled out endlessly, mile upon mile of seemingly eternal dry wilderness with roaming herds of game dotted about in the distance. As they approached the Olduvai Gorge, the Landrover had to negotiate its own path through a rugged ascent into the Ngorongoro Crater - where, amongst prehistoric fossilized remains of extinct creatures, the famous first skull of man was found by Louis and Mary Leakey. And here, too, they were all privileged to witness what their safari was all about... flamingos, lions and rhinoceroses sauntered leisurely in their own territory as they gasped in total delight. Even for Carole, it was a sight that would forever thrill her.

However, she had to confess that despite their overwhelming excitement at seeing these magnificent wild animals in their natural habitat, they also succumbed to a great amount of giggling and fooling around, rather like three St Trinian schoolgirls on the loose! Their poor guide seemed confused and perplexed over their behaviour, but happily drove them through the four days of their safari through the Olduvai Gorge, up to and through the Lake Manyara National Park, where they saw gazelles, wildebeest and zebras, and finally back to Arusha.

All too soon, their memorable holiday was over and they boarded the flight back to Dar es Salaam. Nick surprised his wife by being at the airport to welcome them back having just recently returned from his business trip in Botswana, but of course, Joy was his sister and no doubt he was happy to see her. The last week of Joy and Eunice's stay in Africa was spent idly relaxing at home, baking in the hot sun, lazing on the local beach and swimming in the sea where Carole was able to boast her new ability of floating on water (which for some reason she found infinitely easier than swimming!).

Also, Carole spent many hours talking through and planning her forthcoming return to England; Eunice had brought the necessary paperwork to finalize Pinky's quarantine preparations and travel arrangements were then completed. Pinky would have to be boarded for six months before being able to join them as a family pet again.

As Eunice and Joy left to return home, it was hard to believe that the next time they would meet, she, too, would be back in England, with Marc and Victoria - for good.

Nick and Carole were now sadly resigned to their separation. He loved another woman and would not end the affair to keep his family together. Anyway, it had gone beyond that. Trust had been destroyed. And Carole had changed, become more independent, outspoken, stronger - and was no longer sure she would want to try again even if given the chance. But there at least remained a thin thread of affection which would enable them to maintain good contact for the children's sake. She no longer felt bitter, angry or sorry for herself, just preoccupied with her own survival; impatient now to move onwards, prove to herself of what she was capable.

Pinky's departure date drew nearer. Her inoculations, medical certificate and health report were all in order and a transport container prepared for the journey. In fact she had already been sleeping in the bottom half of the container to accustom her to it.

Finally the day arrived. June 23rd. Poor Pinky, so unsuspecting, her little tail wagging with excitement as they piled her into the back of the car. Marc and Victoria stayed behind, their eyes brimming with tears as they kissed her goodbye.

95

'See you next week,' they promised, fondling her velvet ears.

See you next week!!

It was unbelievably true. Carole couldn't believe it. Their own flight to England was just five days ahead and she wondered for the umpteenth time what on earth the future held in store for them.

Carole and Nick took Pinky to the airport. They arrived at the Cargo Terminal to be told the flight was delayed by several hours. This was crucial. An official from the kennel's quarantine department would be waiting for Pinky's arrival so Carole had to make a frantic phone call to Leicester warning of the delay with the assurance she would phone again as soon as the plane had taken off.

Several hours later, the flight was ready for departure. They fastened Pinky into her container, piled it with newspaper, blankets and a few of her favourite toys and left her with the other cargo for transportation.

No longer did her little tail wag.

Frightened eyes fixed pleadingly on them as they tried to offer a casual farewell.

'See you soon, Pinky,' choked Carole.

Nick gave a small wave and quickly turned away. He didn't know when or even if he would ever see her again. They stayed at the passenger terminal, watching every item of cargo loaded onto the plane until Pinky's container - the very last item on the trailer - was finally on board. Carole phoned Leicester to tell them Pinky was on her way, and they left with very heavy hearts.

Everything was now rushing towards a grand finale. Victoria, Marc and Carole were frantically packing what belongings they could into suitcases. Nick hovered in the background, watching, silent, uncertain and insecure. Carole had phoned the kennels in Leicestershire to learn that Pinky had arrived safely, a little distressed and travel weary but had since enjoyed a good night's sleep and a full dinner. Thank goodness that bit was over.

All their friends and neighbours now knew she was leaving with the children. It came as something of a shock to them because although it was undoubtedly understood she and Nick were having problems, no-one was aware they were separating. Consequently, the last three nights were spent bidding social farewells. The children, too, had friends to say goodbye to, with 'Miss Dar es Salaam' in particular having to disentangle her heart from a pack of bereft admirers.

On Friday June 28th 1985, they all rose early. The dawn sun flooded through the windows as Carole looked around the house for the last time. Somehow she felt too calm to be true. Was it disbelief? Numbness? They loaded the Landrover with all their suitcases and by six o'clock were ready to leave for the airport. Local neighbours had also risen early to wish Carole and the children the best of luck, with one lovelorn fan of Victoria's weeping bitterly as Nick pulled slowly away in the car. The three of them waved until they were all out of sight, but still, she was strangely unemotional.

Nick was silent, driving with his eyes fixed ahead; just a tightness in his jaw belied the brave exterior. Carole felt sorry for him. He was losing so much; was this really what he wanted? She looked at his hands on the steering wheel, brown, lean, strong hands - and for some reason suddenly remembered looking at those same hands gripped to the wheel on the way back from Mufindi in April 1982 when he had first said 'I think I love her.'

This very point in time stemmed from that moment. Those words had changed her life - their lives. Over three years ago. And still he loved her. And during those three years she had been diagnosed with Hodgkin's Disease, endured a gruelling year of treatment. She even felt her cancer had stemmed from those words.

How strange life was.

One day everything can be fine, life plodding along in its normal, predictable routine - and then another day something totally unexpected can suddenly happen to throw it all completely off course, never to be the same again.

But right now, there was no predictable, routine path to follow. It was like stepping into a blank void. Some kind of survival instinct held her in calm control and by the time they arrived at the airport she was totally in charge of the situation.

Within half an hour, they had passed through customs and had their luggage boarded; shortly after it was time for them to alight. Nick hugged Victoria and Marc and then turned to his wife.

'Bye,' he said, squeezing Carole so tightly she could hardly breathe.

She pulled herself away, still strangely unemotional, and shepherded the children onto the plane. Finally, Carole threw one last glance behind her and caught sight of Nick, so alone, waving, his eyes full of pain.

He told her years later that he had then got into the Landrover, driven to a secluded spot and broken his heart.

CHAPTER NINETEEN

There, This is You Now

Victoria, Marc and Carole walked through the front door of the cosy, two bedroomed terraced house in Enderby on Friday evening, June 28th 1985, 'home' now until they found a place of their own.

Mum and dad had met them at Heathrow Airport and driven them all back to Leicestershire. There had been little enough room in the car for five plus all their belongings, but now, too, the poor little house bulged at the seams. Carole's parents elbowed their way through to the kitchen to put the kettle on as the three of them stepped over bags, squeezed past suitcases and manoeuvred around one another in an attempt to organize themselves.

If living space was at a premium, then sleeping arrangements were even more so. Marc and Victoria would have to share Carole's parents' bedroom. Carole herself would be wedged amongst cartons and suitcases in the tiny box room while mum and dad moved downstairs. It was immensely awkward for all of them, but especially for Carole's mum and dad who didn't deserve such inconvenience. They had already done more than enough for her. But she was so happy now to be back, so grateful to be there.

After a surprisingly good night's comfortable sleep, Carole awoke refreshed and energetic. Her first preoccupation was to phone the boarding kennels and find out how Pinky was. They reassured her she was fine, had settled down well, but advised her not to visit just yet as it would probably disturb her. Poor Pinky. Restrained for six months in a kennel and small run. Obviously she couldn't be exercised outside her limited confines as that would defeat the object of quarantine, but how Carole longed to have her back again. It would be Christmas before she could join them.

After a light breakfast, Victoria, Marc and Carole trooped off into Leicester. It was mum and dad's Ruby wedding anniversary the next day and Carole wanted to buy them a celebratory present. After careful consideration, they chose a beautiful china tea set painted with delicate ruby coloured flowers. They then bought appropriate wrapping paper and card before splashing out on a few clothes for themselves.

The next item on her agenda was to approach an estate agent with a view to looking at the housing market. She and Nick had agreed on a small amount of capital which hopefully would enable the three of them to find their own modest living accommodation. Carole came away befuddled with legalities and half a dozen property details.

Back home at her parents' house, she phoned the cargo warehouse agency that had shipped over a huge crate of belongings to be told she would have to wait for clearance before being able to collect it. They suggested she call again on Monday.

Monday.

A shiver ran up her spine.

Carole had almost forgotten her appointment with Dr Khanna was on Monday. However, to round off her Saturday, she spent the evening with Eunice. The last time they had been together was in Dar es Salaam when she and Joy had spent a last opportune holiday with her there. Strange to think Africa had then been her home. A beautiful country - but no longer her homeland. Maybe it never had been.

Her first full day back. And for Victoria and Marc too. In her little box room about to go to sleep, the phone rang. It was Nick just checking they had all arrived safely.

'Hope everything goes well for you on Monday,' he added, 'I'll be in touch again soon.'

Carole's sleep was disturbed that night. Dreams were a confusion of hospitals and hyenas, of Nick, Eunice, tea sets, estate agents and a palm fringed coastline. In the background, she could hear Victoria and Marc asking where the yachts were moored at the Enderby Village Hall. She awoke troubled but put it all behind her. Sunday - it was mum and dad's Ruby wedding anniversary and the house was to be filled even more with friends and relatives joining in the celebration.

The next day Carole had her appointment at the Leicester Royal Infirmary. It had been six months since her last check up. So much had happened in between that it had been largely pushed to the back of her mind. But now, the whole disease loomed again like a black cloud to remind her how vulnerable she still was. For some reason Carole felt particularly insecure. Perhaps because of other things, she hadn't mentally prepared herself for another examination, or maybe she'd been so preoccupied with her emotional wellbeing it was now a shock to remember there had once been an even bigger fight for survival.

She tormented herself with a completely fabricated premonition that Dr Khanna would find some irregularity - some lump, or a suspicious blood count. Then what would happen?

But it was all negative thinking. Dr Khanna seemed most delighted with her progress and a further appointment was made for January 1986. Free again! The relief was enormous! However, as she looked around the waiting area at the sea of anxious faces come to see Dr Khanna, she suddenly felt a huge surge of compassion towards them all. Strange. She wanted to hold their frightened hands and say 'don't worry, you'll be okay.'

All well and good to think like this now, she told herself with an inward smile, but she had hardly been a paragon of human strength in the past! Goodness, another reprieve - and she considered herself a shining example of courage and bravery.

Perhaps more to the point, it was Victoria and Marc who deserved acknowledgement for their strength. They had supported her and uprooted themselves without faltering; and now, in less than ideal conditions they were getting on with life in a cheerful, optimistic manner. Both of them had re-established contact with old friends and Victoria had somehow managed to acquire a male admirer in record breaking time!

In fact, it was Victoria who directed her mother towards a semi-detached house for sale just outside the village. Carole had scoured the estate agent's property guide without much enthusiasm, but eyeing the place Victoria had seen, she had to agree it looked quite suitable. She noted the phone number on the For Sale board, and called to make an appointment to view.

Meanwhile, the cargo agency phoned to say her crate had received clearance and was ready for collection. This was going to be far too big to get in the boot of a car and she was rescued by an offer from Pete, who, with Marianne, volunteered to collect the crate in his own large trailer. The crate was so large and heavy that the cargo had to be opened and off loaded in the street, a bit at a time, then taken into her parents' home - subjecting them to further cramped chaos.

It was important not to take too long finding a place of their own, for mum and dad's sake as much as anyone's.

Carole had an appointment to view the house and duly called at the arranged time. A young man, about her own age, invited Carole in and showed her around. It was necessary to find somewhere that needed no improvement and with as many fixtures and fittings as possible, and it so happened the house proved ideal. Unfortunately, the asking price was rather more than she could afford and so reluctantly she had to turn the offer down.

'Well, perhaps your husband would like to view before you make a final decision,' persuaded the owner, his manner particularly warm and open.

'Mmm, really it's up to me,' Carole explained. 'I'm on my own now, just looking for a place for myself and the children.'

The young man nodded sympathetically. He, too, was selling because of a marriage breakdown.

'Just have a think about it and let me know.'

She did think about it and decided to phone him later that night with an offer £1000 less than his asking price.

'Er..,' he hesitated, 'Okay - you can have it for £1000 less if you'll go out for a drink with me.'

Carole was completely taken aback at this unexpected twist in negotiations but dazedly heard herself agreeing to it! After she put the phone down, she flopped heavily into a chair, her mind whizzing, heart racing and face flushed. Giggling like a sixteen year old, she laughed at the absurdity of it all. She was going to buy her own, first home and had just accepted her first date in over fifteen years!

His name was John.

He'd been married for eight years when his wife had left him for another man. He had two young daughters who he missed terribly. John told Carole all this as they sat in a Leicestershire country pub, her knees trembling in adolescent-type nervousness. Even as she quaked innocently, her conscience was riddled with guilt. It needn't have been, she was perfectly entitled to go out with John, but it felt so naughty! Carole kept him respectably at a safe distance, but nevertheless thoroughly enjoyed his company and they arranged a further date for the weekend.

This time, Carole was much more relaxed. They chatted comfortably together in the same pub, Carole telling him her life story and them both exchanging future hopes and plans. Later, they went back to his place - soon to be hers.

Low lights and soft music created a seductive atmosphere, and Carole felt deliciously aware of her own femininity and independence. John caressed her hand, fingering her wedding ring, still in its redundant, but once loyal place.

'Why do you still wear your wedding ring?' he asked.

She shrugged her shoulders as if to imply indifference. In truth, she still wore it to avoid severing the link with her past, a kind of symbolic admission of not quite letting go.

'Let me take it off for you now.'

Willingly now, she let him slip the ring down her finger then held up her strangely naked hand for them both to see.

'There, this is you now,' he said.

The act was significant and the whole evening became a turning point in her life. Suddenly she *felt* single. And she liked it. She was answerable to no-one; she was in charge of her own life; she could do whatever she wanted.

And she wanted to enjoy herself.

CHAPTER TWENTY

Another Kind of Bird

Carole saw John just a couple more times, but predominantly to finalize the sale of his house with a moving date planned for October 18th, three months ahead.

Socially, she was spreading her new wings. She had married so young, and from the tender age of fifteen had always been faithful to Nick. It was perhaps hardly surprising that she now had this youthful energy to sow belated wild oats! And she felt so well, so full of vitality - healthier than ever before in her life. Her parents were delighted to see their daughter so vibrantly happy and positively welcomed her active night life. Victoria at sixteen, and Marc, fifteen, were also coming and going at various times of the day and night. The house was totally without order, routine, mealtimes or discipline, but Carole's mum and dad sat back regardless, maybe taking the frequent desertions from 'base camp' as precious snatched breaths of peace and quiet.

In September, Carole went alone to see Pinky.

It was a heart rending reunion that hurt them both. She looked well enough, but her excitement at seeing Carole turned to absolute despair for both of them when she turned to leave. If only she could have explained the situation to her, but as it was, she felt downright cruel.

But September was also a time for reflecting on the past. It was exactly two years ago she had been fighting for her life when, in the middle of chemotherapy, an extracted tooth had resulted in septicaemia. If someone had told her then how she would be feeling now, she would never, ever have believed them.

It went to show that even in the darkest hour, there had to be hope.

Carole's 'hope' may have been a blatant, overt enjoyment of post adolescent mischief - but as the candle slowly began to burn down, an adult need for a more meaningful relationship started to grow. It was perhaps the wrong time, too soon maybe, for her to see Nick again, but an occasion arose which prompted a puzzling reaction within her. One afternoon the phone rang.

'Hello?' she said.

'Hi - it's me, Nick.'

'*Nick!* Carole was genuinely pleased. 'Where are you?'

'Just ten minutes walk away, at my mother's.'

This was totally unexpected. She had absolutely no idea he had planned on coming to England, let alone Enderby. Adrenaline surged through her as she suddenly felt a mixture of dread and excitement.

'Can I come round to see you?' he added apprehensively.

Carole was completely thrown off balance. Did she want to see him? She heard herself employ a delaying tactic then agreed for herself to go round and visit him which somehow seemed more under her control. Half an hour later she rang the doorbell.

Nick greeted her with a warm hug, and stared approvingly into her eyes.

'You look well,' he nodded, smiling.

It felt weird seeing him knowing what she had been up to in the last three months.

'So, what have you been doing with yourself?' he asked.

Shrugging her shoulders to pass that by, she turned the question round.

'How about you?'

Nick told her Lynn had left her husband over two months ago, spending an English summer with her children at a family base in Yorkshire and using the time to decide which man to return to. Her husband or Nick. This greatly surprised Carole as she had expected Lynn to move in with Nick as soon as her back was turned. She hadn't envisaged any doubts.

'I'm on my way to visit her, after staying with Terry and Karen for the weekend.' Nick hesitated. 'Would you like to come with me to see Terry and Karen?'

Carole froze. She was muddled. Nick seemed lonely, vulnerable. She was the one enjoying sexual adventures and independence.

But why not go? It would be good to see Terry and Karen and she was sure her parents wouldn't mind keeping an eye on the children.

'Mmm. Yes, that sounds okay - but I'll just need to check with mum and dad.'

They were perfectly agreeable to her going, maybe hoping for a reconciliation, and so later that day they found themselves driving to Chelmsford to see their old friends. Terry and Karen were delighted to see them together again. However, their relationship was not discussed even when Carole asked for separate sleeping accommodation, and the four of them enjoyed a most lighthearted, entertaining weekend.

On the return journey to Leicester, it was obvious Nick was stimulated by Carole's outward confidence and assertiveness. He questioned her and she told him more than he bargained for. Confused, hurt and yet surprised, his sulky reprimands were mixed with arousal. They arrived back at his parents' empty house in the middle of the afternoon and finally sealed the end of their marriage in the same room, in the same bed as they had first begun it, sweetly, naively, clumsily over half a lifetime ago.

Afterwards, Carole lay there staring at the ceiling with a satisfaction that was emotional as much as physical. She didn't want Nick back, she reflected, and now it was her turn to feel like the mistress stealing another woman's lover.

Satisfying, but not comfortable.

That wasn't what she wanted and she knew it would never happen again.

Victoria and Marc joined Carole on her next visit to see Pinky. It was difficult knowing what was best for the dog - indeed, for all of them, but she considered it important for the children to see Pinky as they kept insisting. It was the first time Pinky had seen them since she had been piled unsuspectingly into the back of Nick's car with the children's farewell kisses still moist on her face.

Bless her, she remembered them as if it had been yesterday! Tail wagging, huge grin, tongue lolling, she twisted and wriggled in absolute submissive ecstasy. Marc and Victoria were most relieved to see she hadn't forgotten them. Carole knew, of course, that she would never forget them. After all, she had been gone a whole year and yet Pinky had remembered her instantly on her return. But again, it was agony wrenching themselves away. The poor dog must have wondered why she couldn't come with them and Carole vowed then to limit visits to a minimum for all their sakes.

Carole felt, too, it would help them as a family to have Pinky home. Victoria was showing a few signs of emotional disturbance, and both children were struggling with their new comprehensive schools. Victoria in particular was having problems owing to a change of examination board halfway through her 'O' levels. She felt inadequate and rebelled by choosing friends that her mother considered less academically able. Carole sensed, too, that both Marc and Victoria were missing Africa.

For herself, she was beginning to burn out from her high flying social frivolities, and there sometimes threatened a void of loneliness. She still felt very well physically, but every now and again the future looked rather hollow.

One night, a girlfriend called Beverley phoned inviting Carole to stay for the weekend at her place near Peterborough with the idea of going to the opening of a new nightclub nearby. Carole really didn't feel like it. She had already been out several nights in succession - but she hadn't seen Beverley since the break up of both their respective marriages, and so she agreed.

Fortunately, they had exchanged most of their personal histories before entering the club, which was just as well as the deafening music, flashing psychedelic lights and claustrophobic atmosphere made further conversation impossible. Gyrating amongst a jam packed floor of bodies, Beverley and Carole soon decided they would rather sit down. Even so, it was difficult to talk. By midnight, Beverley had started to develop a slight headache so they decided to have one last drink and leave.

'Don't look now,' said Beverley as they finally emptied their glasses, 'but there's a man over there who hasn't taken his eyes off you.'

Contrary to her advice, Carole immediately turned her head in the direction Beverley had indicated and locked into the gaze of a most attractive, warm, smiling face. He acknowledged her attention with a questioning nod of his head towards the dance floor.

'Do you mind if I have just one dance, Beverley?' she asked, remembering her friend's headache.

'No, you go ahead,' she smiled.

Regardless of the cramped space, they made themselves a small area and shouted fragments of conversation at one another as they danced. His name was Paul, he worked for the RAF and was just back from Cyprus; he had travelled a great deal - and something about him interested Carole. However, she was bothered about Beverley and after the dance, thanked him and turned away. With charm and persistence, Paul smiled, but returned with her to join Beverley and helped negotiate plans for the rest of the evening.

'I've got a thumping headache,' Beverley apologized, 'do you mind if I go home?'

As Beverley was the driver, and Carole was staying at her place, it really meant she had to leave with her.

'Perhaps I can take you back later,' suggested Paul, 'if that's okay with you, Beverley?'

It was fine with her, so Beverley left to go home, and she and Paul stayed until closing time at two o'clock. They had so much to talk about that later, when they eventually arrived at Beverley's, she took the liberty of inviting him in for coffee. Tip-toeing around and talking in whispers, they gossiped without pause until the clinking of milk bottles was heard on the doorstep.

Something strange had happened.

Although a virtual stranger, Carole felt as if she'd known this man all her life. It seemed so natural, so comfortable - like a long lost friend she'd been waiting to meet up with for years. There was so much talking to catch up on, exchanging of ideas, experiences and thoughts - and not enough hours left in the night to share with him.

Paul, too, found their meeting meaningful and was reluctant to leave.

'I shall have to go,' he moaned, 'it's already morning and I have to drive up to Stornaway in a few hours! I shall be back on Thursday. Perhaps we can see each other then.'

Carole rummaged around in her bag for paper and pen to swap names and phone numbers. After scribbling down her own details, she passed him some paper.

'What's this?' she exclaimed after reading what he'd written.

'What's what?'

'This… your name, your surname!'

'Why? It's Bird,' he admitted puzzled.

'*Bird??!!*.

'Yes…Bird,'

Poor Paul looked worried, confused. What was wrong?

But for Carole, the coincidence was just too much to bear. Slowly, the funny side of it tickled her sense of humour and a big smile spread across her face. This was incredible! How meaningful! Paul stared at her, smiling hesitantly yet unsure as to what the joke was about, but by now Carole was laughing helplessly and shaking her head in disbelief.

'Well, well!' she gasped, 'I think that must be some kind of omen!'

She fell into his arms, open, responsive, safe - and knew then, for sure, that someone very special had just flown into her life.

CHAPTER TWENTY-ONE

Long Term Plans?

Within four weeks Carole's life had done a complete about turn. She was in love - and in her own home.

There she was, sprawled all over the settee, *her* settee, in *her* living room in *her* house. Boxes, cartons, bags, cases and dustbin liners full of miscellaneous bits and pieces spilled throughout the rooms - *her* rooms, reminding her fleetingly of when she'd finally returned back to Dar es Salaam to a vaguely similar scene after completing hospital treatment. Only this time, although it might appear a shambles, everything was, in fact, methodically packed and labelled.

'Do you want a cup of tea?' called Paul from the kitchen amidst the sound of clattering crockery and tearing cardboard.

'I think champagne would be more in order, but tea will do for now!'

Lovely Paul. Since she'd met him little more than a month ago, her life had been turned upside down yet again. Only this time, it was decidedly for the better. They had instantly and easily grown close, an immediate, loving friendship that was growing more deeply by the day. Eunice worried for her friend's emotional welfare and urged her to exercise caution. Marc and Victoria had looked on warily, but seemed to be accepting him - although Victoria was still showing rebellious signs of disturbed behaviour from leaving dad and Dar es Salaam. She guessed they all had their own traumas to work through, and sometimes Carole felt guilty with her own selfish preoccupations. After all, they had so supportingly elected to join her, was she now neglecting them?

Right then, on Moving Day, both children were staying with Carole's mum and dad just five minutes walk away. They would be round later when hopefully there would be more semblance of order around the place!

Paul triumphantly emerged, grinning, with a retrieved tray, two mugs of steaming tea and a few biscuits.

'Not quite our thatched cottage in the country,' he said wistfully, casting his eyes around the room, 'but not bad for a single woman.'

'Next time!' laughed Carole, gratefully taking the welcome drink off the tray. This place was definitely home for just Victoria, Marc and herself. They had struggled hard and suffered a lot to earn this independence. It was not going to be easily relinquished nor intruded upon lightly. And they had Christmas 1985 with Pinky to look forward to; a very personal, family triumph in itself!

The four of them, Paul, Marc, Victoria and Carole had been over to see Pinky one last time. She had remembered the three of them instantly, wagging her tail and licking them in wet, wiggly enthusiasm. She had looked well but there was no mistaking the sorrowful confusion in her eyes as they left. They would not go again now until December 24th, Christmas Eve, when they would bring her back home with them for good.

Carole wanted Pinky back so much. Not only did they all yearn for her, Carole especially, but she felt Pinky could link them all, unite them somehow through a common bond of love and make the family feel more complete again.

By the beginning of November, their new house was pretty well organized. It was good having space, privacy and independence again, though Carole was more than indebted to her parents for providing an invaluable lifeline. Marc had now settled down well at the county comprehensive and was voicing an interest in joining the army on leaving school. With Paul being in the RAF, they had plenty to talk about and had grown quite close.

Victoria, on the other hand, had resorted to complaining loudly and bitterly about her schooling, and was furiously abusive on the change of 'O' level syllabus mid-stream, which undoubtedly was an unfortunate handicap. She had also turned to slamming doors at home, hurling rebellious attacks at authority and spitting venomous resentment towards her father for having to live in this 'shitty hell-hole'. Her relationship with a rather dubious character had glued into a supportive bond which on one hand probably worsened matters, yet on the other maybe held her together. The crunch came when she wanted *out* of home and school, preferring to share her life with the boyfriend in a small bedsit. Carole begged her to wait until after Christmas and pleaded with her to finish her exams. She agreed half-heartedly but it was very much a part-time daughter who accompanied them all to collect Pinky on Christmas Eve day.

Christmas had grown to mean a lot to Carole. It had thrown up some fairly poignant emotions in the past and it felt important to make it happy. After all, she *was* happy! She felt brilliantly well, had her own house, the children were with her (just!), there was Paul, Eunice and her parents were nearby - and now, they were finally going to fetch Pinky back!

Their home was lavishly decorated with Christmas trimmings and a huge, real Christmas tree adorned the living room, sparkling with lights, glitter and tinsel. Paul had his own flat some 25 miles away, but they all wanted him to stay with them over Christmas. The floor at the base of the tree was teasingly stacked with presents; the fridge was bulging with an enormous turkey and the kitchen overflowed with chestnuts, fruit and wine. Most importantly, a large dog bowl, already full of fresh water, established new presence on the kitchen floor. And next to that, a soft, clean blanket lined a generously sized dog basket.

It had been exactly six months ago to the day, June 24th, that Pinky had landed in England following her flight from Dar es Salaam. Now, as Paul drove them to the boarding kennels for the last time, she remembered that hot, sunny, sad day, when she and Nick had piled an excited dog into the back of the car, so unsuspecting, so trusting - only to end up secured in a crate as cargo in the base of an aeroplane followed by six months quarantine, confined to a cage and small run in strange surroundings.

Poor Pinky.

Her thoughts too, turned to Nick. She wondered if he would think about this day, the last day of Pinky's quarantine, and remember her. Then she thought of Nick and Lynn. What were they doing this Christmas? Carole sighed deeply, pain never too far away. Would she ever by truly free of hurt?

'Oh, I'm so excited!' squealed Victoria in the back of the car, 'I just can't *wait* to see her!'

Carole twisted round to smile at her, and saw both Victoria and Marc flushed with anticipation. With increasing resilience (and practice), she dropped the past and rejoined the children in their impatient enthusiasm.

'I can't wait, either,' she said.

When they arrived at the kennels, Pinky was ready to be collected. Various papers had been prepared, Carole just had to sign a document and then she was free to take their dog away. As it was only a family saloon car, Pinky, with all her abounding enthusiasm, had to share the back seat with the children but no-one complained. Although Pinky's world had suddenly expanded by overwhelming proportions, she took it totally in her stride. Once home, it took ten minutes of rapid circling, licking, jumping and tail crashing to dismiss six months of quarantine into history. It was as if they had just collected her from friends after some local shopping. Indeed, she walked into the kitchen - straight to the water bowl for a refreshing slosh and slurp - with no more than a cursory glance around and an 'mm, this'll do,' before curling up into her new basket for a much wished for snooze.

Dogs, Carole decided, had quite a different concept of separation, time and place to humans!

Christmas was good. She knew she was using it as a yardstick for the future, having become quite superstitious about that time of year, and, as she had an appointment with Dr Khanna for 13th January (1986) she was clinging to every hopeful indication that all was well. Obviously, Paul knew all about her cancer by then. They sometimes hinted tentative plans on a long-term future together, though both fought possessively for independence, but it was only fair he knew the score. And the truth was that, at worst, she was still at risk from a relapse, and at best, for what it mattered, was most likely infertile.

But it was Eunice who came with her for her appointment with Dr Khanna in the new year. Carole had this overwhelming urge to care for other cancer sufferers again. She'd had this briefly before, when she'd last seen Dr Khanna and seen the sea of anxious faces in the waiting room. For Carole, it was a kind of gratitude for being alive - though she was still far from home and dry; but still she felt she could be of some use, surely, to someone? Eunice, as a nurse, felt this an area where she, too, would like to help.

The tests were fine and Dr Khanna was pleased with her, commenting on how well she looked. A further appointment was made for September 22nd that year, over eight months away!

By the end of January, both Carole and Eunice had volunteered their caring services to a charitable organization called 'Coping with Cancer', a supportive network in Leicester which offers practical, informative and emotional help to sufferers and friends and relatives, undertaking a four week induction course to help them on their way.

Meanwhile, back at home, Carole's part-time daughter continued to be a problem, every straightforward conversation somehow ending up a battle of wills. Carole relented every time, partly because she felt somewhat to blame and partly because she thought she would lose her altogether if she wasn't careful. She knew Victoria was still there somewhere deep inside - but it felt as if no-one could reach that bit anymore. Her boyfriend was the largest part of her life, education and career now dissolving fast into futile insignificance.

Marc, on the other hand, was carefully planning his future and working hard towards a career in the army. His school work was progressing well and he had joined the local army cadets. Paul joined them every weekend, often spending considerable time with Marc, fishing or shooting or sharing military tales over a beery lemonade.

Their own moments together had deepened the relationship into definite long-term plans, and they now often dreamt of the future, of the children being older and settled contentedly, of Carole being totally free of cancer and of the two of them living happily ever after in an old, thatched country cottage.

If only...

CHAPTER TWENTY-TWO

Windrush Cottage

Health-wise, it seemed that Carole was in excellent form, in fact better now than everybody else, including Pinky.

Her parents were having a few problems. Dad was having leg pains and mum was suffering bouts of indigestion. Carole guessed she'd put them through it a bit, and it was unfortunately understandable they might suffer from stress. She was pleased to be nearby and often popped in for a chat and to check they were okay.

Pinky was adorable but she was suffering from occasional breathlessness. Carole thought that if it carried on she would get it checked out at the vets. Most likely though, she decided, she was out of condition from lack of exercise in the kennels.

Eunice and Carole completed their induction course with the voluntary 'Coping with Cancer' organization and she was soon assigned her first 'client'. Filled with caring intentions, she befriended her poor cancer victim in her own home. She was a lovely, middle aged lady, unfortunately suffering from a terminal stage of cancer and in desperate need of emotional support.

Carole was useless.

Within minutes of being there to offer comfort and company, all her so-called strength had diminished. She felt scared and vulnerable. Hopefully, she feigned caring empathy and optimism but no sooner was she out of the front door than she crawled away, flooded with too recent a memory from her own illness to be of any constructive use to man nor beast for quite a while yet.

Eunice meanwhile, became a valuable member of the organization for many months after Carole's hasty exit and must have offered a lot of comfort to many. Eventually she took a course in Marie Curie nursing (round the clock care for the terminally ill).

The whole experience shook Carole up. To make matters worse, problems with Victoria came to head with the final slamming of the front door as she blasted off to go and live with her boyfriend. Her flunked 'O' levels stained potential career plans, of which she had none anyway, and Carole felt hopeless and helpless over her future.

Pinky once again became a loyal shoulder to weep on; the perfect listener who passed neither advice nor judgement. But there was something definitely wrong with Pinky, too.

It was almost June. She had been back with them nearly six months now, and her breathing was increasingly laboured with even the minimum amount of exercise. This, in turn, was giving her a weight problem and all in all, she was no longer a healthy dog. Carole made an appointment with the vet who thought obesity could be the cause - but he didn't like the sound of her heart. Could he have her in for a day for exploratory tests?

Carole was frightened.

Not Pinky - oh no.

They had been through too much together. She was terrified at the thought of losing her.

'Just routine tests,' the vet assured her, 'I'm sure there's nothing to be alarmed about.'

Of course, there was no choice and so poor Pinky was admitted for a day to explore any potential problems. The outcome was horrendous although the vet was so excited he could hardly control a morbid enthusiasm.

'She has heartworm,' he informed Carole later that day as she went to collect her. 'For myself, I have never heard of heartworm in this country. It's a tropical disease, she must have been infected in Tanzania.'

She looked at him in disbelief.

'Can you treat it?'

'I'm not sure. You see, her heart is actually engorged with this lethal parasite. We need to kill the worm which actually thrives and grows within the heart. Eventually,' the vet continued, 'the size of the parasite becomes so large it suffocates its victim by totally constricting the flow of blood. Already, in Pinky's case, the problem is well advanced which, I regret, complicates matters.'

'Surely, they should have picked this up when she was in quarantine?'

His reply was guarded and non-committal.

'Mmm. It should have been easy to find through a straightforward blood test, even in the early stages. But we have to remember she wasn't being quarantined for medical research - just as an elimination process to rule out specific infectious diseases.'

'What do you suggest, then?' Carole asked, hardly hearing her own, calculated voice.

'We'll try and save her,' he nodded soberly. 'We'll do our best. It's not so much destroying the worm, but flushing the disintegrated bits out of the system afterwards without causing a thrombosis that poses the gravest risk.'

'I see,' she murmured, and followed the sorry consultation with an appointment for Pinky's unavoidable surgery.

With heavy heart, she led Pinky, still wobbly and unsteady but ever trusting into the car. They got home and Carole tucked her up in her bed, and she dozily fell into a deep slumber.

'Oh, Pinky,' Carole sobbed, laying down beside her and burying her face into her warm, golden fur, 'oh, Pinky, don't die. I love you too much! I can't live without you.'

She just sighed and slept.

At this low ebb, Carole's friend, Marianne, phoned up for a chat. Carole poured out her troubles about Victoria and her boyfriend, she revealed the saga of 'Coping with Cancer' and her uselessness as a supportive counsellor and finally told her about Pinky's heartworm.

It was Marianne who had previously instigated psychic healing for Carole whilst researching alternative therapy and they had followed that with classes on the 'Great White Light'.

'Why don't you come along to Win Wood's Friday night 'Positive Thinking and Awareness Classes'?' she now suggested.

Through Marianne, she had seen Win Wood before for natural healing and reflexology and found her very genuine in her care for others. Perhaps marginally more orthodox in her thinking than some it suddenly seemed a comforting thought.

'Mmm. Why not?' she agreed, mentally dragging Eunice along with her, 'sounds a good idea.'

Eunice was delighted at the prospect, being a strict advocate of positive thought. Moreover, the weekly sessions promised to touch on spirit communication, an area of personal interest and intrigue since Carole's friends, Doris and Barbara, cancer patients from the old Friday morning chemotherapy sessions, had revealed their own 'near-death experiences.'

The classes also provided thought provoking fun whilst a dozen or so 'students' dabbled in experimental telepathy, prayer, meditation, healing, psychometry, visualization and positive mind control.

There was undoubtedly something to be gained from this whole alternative way of thinking, though both Eunice and Carole were often inattentive and giggly pupils, never quite producing the much hoped for paranormal results! However, talking to Win Wood after the class did a lot to reaffirm Carole's private thoughts that death was nothing to fear and certainly not the end. It was a revelation she had arrived at through personal awareness and the experience of others, especially those gravely ill, but there was great comfort and strength to be gained by sharing what was still often an inhibited subject. It was also a great comfort to believe they had some measure of control by exercising positive thought.

Paul laughed at it all. But Carole definitely drew on positivity and healing prayer when it came to Pinky's operation. And who knows what contribution it made?

The fact was, she made it!

She survived not only the operation but the following crucial twenty-four hours while disintegrating pieces of parasite entered her bloodstream and got naturally flushed away. The vet stayed with her throughout the night, as determined as they all were that she should survive. All the care, dedication, skill, prayers and positive thought paid off and she was eventually allowed home to recover.

He was a young vet, newly out of training and he used Pinky's case to write up a report which, at the time, was kept available at an English university for reference. He was particularly pleased, as a freshly qualified veterinary surgeon, to have had the experience of successfully treating heartworm in this country.

On Pinky's return home, she was introduced to Thumper, a twelve week old kitten Carole had recently been given by Marianne. They quickly and rather surprisingly found loving intimacy in one another, Thumper nestling into Pinky's warm, recuperating body.

A positive attitude was needed again when a routine cervical smear test showed that Carole had irregular cells. Although not immediately a threat, it was not a condition Carole's doctor was happy with and he arranged for her to have a colposcopy (a microscopic examination of the cervix) in January 1987, just a few months away.

Meanwhile, at the end of September, she had another routine appointment with Dr Khanna. Paul came with her. She was on the borderline of panic. If it couldn't get her one way, could it get her another? Was she just a clashing, abnormal mass of destructive cells battling against medical intervention; phase it out in one place only to erupt with cancerous irregularity somewhere else?

Carole tried to remember all the tricks of thought she'd acquired for fighting fear. As it happened, Dr Khanna found her in good health with no mention of concern about the colposcopy or anything else. He made an appointment for her to see him the following June with the reassurance that they could then hopefully reduce examinations to once a year.

Temporarily appeased, Carole started to look forward to another Christmas yet again. Victoria and her boyfriend were living together in a small, rented terraced house but happily accepted an invitation to join them for Christmas Day. Marc was now seriously planning to join the army next year, and she and Paul hoped to set up home together in the not too distant future.

As they all raised their glasses over the dinner table that Christmas Day, none of them knew quite what the future held in store for them. Carole had forgotten what a safe, routine and predictable existence could be like - and no doubt, they all wondered where they might be the following year.

'Cheers Pinky!' laughed Victoria, now looking so thin and drained - perhaps the most wounded victim of all from the last few years.

'Cheers Thumper!' echoed Marc.

The animals didn't care about anything except the hopeful possibility of dropped turkey.

Unfortunately, the colposcopy confirmed abnormal cells in the cervix. Sometimes, the irregularity could be easily treated with lasers but for some reason, in Carole's case, it was suggested she have a cone biopsy and an appointment was made for her to be admitted into hospital for five days in June (1987). Again, it was explained to her that at the present time there was absolutely no danger, but if ignored for several years she was at some risk of the cell abnormality becoming cancerous.

Both Carole and Paul had decided to put their respective houses up for sale, so she tried to shelve anxiety on cone biopsies and cell abnormalities for a while and concentrate on future plans. The arrangement between them of him coming over at weekends was no longer enough for them; they wanted to share their lives together under the same roof seven days a week. Paul still had this romantic fantasy of an old, thatched cottage in the country, but even by pooling all their money it seemed an unrealistic dream.

It didn't ease the financial situation by Carole leaving work on May 1st. She had been employed on a part time basis with a local company for several months, but May and June loomed so hectic - they had a holiday in Tenerife booked for the last two weeks in May, followed by Carole's cone biopsy on June 13th, Dr Khanna for June 22nd and, hopefully, the sale of their houses to follow. And then goodness knows where they might live.

Carole's father had been diagnosed as having blocked arteries in his legs, hence the leg pains, and he was booked for an artery by-pass operation in October. Mum continued to suffer quite badly from indigestion and Carole wanted to be around as much as possible to keep an eye on them; they seemed to be plagued with health problems. If it wasn't hers, it was theirs. Would they never be free?

Paul and Carole's two weeks holiday in Tenerife was superb. The glorious May weather was just pleasantly hot and they lazed around for fourteen days, eating, drinking, sunbathing, swimming and sharing dreams of their future together. She was lucky to have met Paul. So kind, attentive and loving. Memories were never far away, but at last she felt able to leave them there, in the past, where they belonged. There was no bitterness left towards Lynn, although admittedly, no warmth either. Her feelings for Nick were confusing; resentment mingled with resignation, hurt with tolerance and loss with gain. She rarely indulged in analysing her feelings, though she did try at least to hold onto the healthy ones and discard the bad, just for the sake of health and sanity. Never did she forget Eunice's reminder of looking after Number One. Herself. And although it might sound selfish, she had a self-preservation instinct that did just that.

The emotional scarring had left her thicker skinned and more independent. Paul, although a few years younger than Carole, was nevertheless a mature man used to his freedom. Somehow, the combination worked well between them, wanting to be together yet respecting each other's space.

On their return to Leicester, Carole had her short stay in hospital to face, which she was dreading out of all proportion. Apparently, there was nothing to worry about, but just the thought of a hospital bed and the prospect of anaesthetic - worse still, feeling sick afterwards - swamped her with sheer, cold panic. For all her personal strength and independence, and for all her spiritual beliefs, hospitals and sickness remained a weakness.

However, she survived. The nurses, as always, were wonderful and this time, she had a regular, daily visitor who bestowed her with love and flowers!

One evening, Paul swept down the ward flushed with excitement, carrying papers in his hand and waving them triumphantly as he reached Carole's bed.

'I've found it!!' he exclaimed, unable to contain his wild enthusiasm.

'Found what?' she asked, confused.

'Look!' he beamed, thrusting the papers at her, 'our cottage!'

Carole's eyes glanced down the dog-eared sheet of paper. At the top, a photographic print showed an old, detached, rural, thatched dwelling in need of renovation.

Underneath were the words:

'Windrush Cottage'.

CHAPTER TWENTY-THREE

Another Move

'We can't afford that!' Carole gasped, without even bothering to look at the asking price.

'Yes we can!' enthused Paul, beaming like a besotted Cheshire cat, 'Look!'

Her eyes scanned the page and fell on a figure just within their range. Still guarded over too much optimism, she queried Paul with suspicious bated breath.

'There must be something wrong with it...'

'No, honestly. Well... I mean it needs a bit of decorating, and the kitchen is awful - and the roof probably needs rethatching, but I've been to see it and it's just right!'

Carole smiled and took his hands in hers. Perhaps, indeed, this was to be their cottage in the country.

After five long days she was discharged home. Paul unfortunately had to go to work which was several miles away. It was so upsetting being forced to wait until the weekend to see Windrush Cottage. Not only was she not yet well enough to drive, but now a heavy blood loss suggested something was wrong.

Carole phoned her mother to ask her advice.

'I don't like the sound of that, love,' she said, 'I think you'd best ring the hospital and see what they say.'

They said she had to be re-admitted, so mum and dad drove her back to the hospital where she stayed for four days after having a burst blood vessel cauterized.

No sooner was she back home again than it was time to see Dr Khanna for her routine appointment.

Carole still hadn't seen Windrush Cottage and now another couple were after it. This had forced Paul into action, and without her having had a chance to view, he'd put in an offer.

This time Carole was more apprehensive than ever over her visit to the Leicester Royal Infirmary. Although it was over four years since the original diagnosis of Hodgkin's Disease and almost three from the end of her treatment, there was always the fear Dr Khanna might find some irregularity.

And what about the cone biopsy?

Would he think a dozen or so chemotherapy sessions an added safety precaution? Might he consider the abnormal cells a serious indication that cancer was just simmering beneath the surface?

Indeed, was it?

Thoughts and fears raced through her mind until she was totally drained. Paul went with her, as anxious as she was, but nevertheless an invaluable source of comfort. In the end, they were both so wound up that when Dr Khanna gave his satisfied verdict they distrusted it.

'You mean everything's okay?' Carole asked hesitantly.

'Yes, I'm quite happy with you.'

'So there's no link between my abnormal cervical smear and Hodgkin's Disease?'

'Absolutely none whatsoever. We'll make your next appointment for a year ahead, June 1988.' And with that she was dismissed. Caringly, but a no nonsense dismissal.

Carole really wanted to spend an hour or two asking him questions, to beg for reassurance, to have him promise it would never come back. But of course, that was impossible. And he didn't want to see her for a whole year! Surely then, she had to be okay? Gradually her anxiety began to fade, replaced by a huge sense of relief and optimism.

By the time Paul and Carole reached the car park, they were both sky high at her progressing to annual check-ups and shifted their thoughts to a total pre-occupation with Windrush Cottage. At long last, she was actually going to see it!

The little old dwelling was about three to four hundred years old, a Grade II listed building, situated on a quiet through road in a sleepy Leicestershire village. Nestled in its own small grounds, its quaint antiquity held a wealth of beams, nooks and crannies; the uneven walls were constructed of wattle and daub and two narrow winding staircases arrived from opposing directions to a rickety three bedroomed first floor. Little leaded windows peeped out onto the meandering country road below and the cottage's own bedraggled garden.

But there, its own beautiful character ended!

In truth, the thatched roof needed completely replacing, every room was in desperate need of decoration - and in parts, repair. The kitchen possessed an old enamel sink and nothing else, and all in all, the house was in a total state of neglect.

Despite the drawbacks, like Paul, she knew it had to be theirs. It was already beginning to look as if Carole's house in Enderby was sold, and Paul too, had a prospective buyer for his property. The other couple who also wanted Windrush Cottage had put in a higher price so unfortunately, they had to offer the full asking amount with an immediate deposit.

Then suddenly it was theirs!

Everything fell neatly into place. Both their own sales went through without a hitch, the council promised a full grant to rethatch the cottage and a moving date was set for September 28th. The rest of the summer was spent excitedly planning their new home and packing belongings into cartons once again!

In August, Marc was accepted for Basic Training with the Signals Corps at Catterick and was due to join them just a few days before the move to Windrush Cottage. Paul and Marc had grown very close, and Carole was pleased that Marc had both of them with him for the all important Open Day before 'signing on'.

Victoria was the one who worried Carole. She rarely saw her, but when she did, it was obvious she wasn't happy. Moreover, she looked so thin with heavy shadows under her eyes and bruises on her body. Yet Carole felt powerless to do anything. Anyway, her boyfriend was always with her - though she did wonder for how much longer. They had bought their own terraced house in Leicester, but the increased mortgage rate had caused financial problems and it was in the throes of being repossessed.

It was shortly to be her eighteenth birthday. Instead of having a happy, carefree youth, she was burdened with problems and misery. Carole's heart ached for her. As her birthday coincided with Marc leaving to join the army and she and Paul moving into the cottage, they had a big family celebration in a country hotel near their new village.

And then Carole noticed something else that worried her. Her mum wasn't eating. At that moment, she put all concern to the back of her mind. After all, mum was probably anxious about dad's by-pass operation next month. Or maybe she, too, had noticed Victoria's obvious poor health. There again, she and Paul were moving next week and would be a good hour's drive away should mum and dad need her. This was certainly bothering Carole and must undeniably have concerned her parents. Nevertheless, they enjoyed a good meal followed by a guided tour through the village and on to Windrush Cottage.

A week later, unbelievably, they were actually living there. It would be a lie to say it all went smoothly. Large items of furniture did not move easily into the small cottage, nor could beds and wardrobes be carried up the narrow, winding stairs without great difficulty, but finally they were in, back once again to the familiar cardboard box conditions she had grown so accustomed to over the years.

Pinky, now just about as fit as she'd ever been, charged ecstatically up one staircase and down the other before reversing the route to her endless delight. Thumper, safely enclosed behind closed windows and doors, sat patiently on the sill, dreaming through the dusty, leaded panes, of mice, fields and freedom.

Paul and Carole toasted their ultimate achievement with champagne.

'Here's to the next umpteen years!' grinned Paul, raising his glass.

'You bet!' concurred Carole, feeling totally, absolutely and thoroughly happy.

Dear God, she prayed silently, please let me have the next umpteen years.

CHAPTER TWENTY-FOUR

An 'Inspirational Story of Triumph'?

A month after they had moved in, Carole's dad went into hospital for his surgery. Following his operation, it was routine procedure to be kept in intensive care for 24 hours with a stay in hospital of at least ten days. It was a hectic time especially now they'd moved 30 miles away, picking up mum, visiting dad and travelling to and fro several times a week.

Mum's legs now had swollen painfully in addition to her persistent stomach problems and she admitted to frequent vomiting. Virtually dragging her by the neck, Carole got her to see her doctor who arranged for her to be admitted into hospital for tests in December.

Dad was discharged, still needing a lot of nursing care and attention which mum was hardly able to give. Anyway, she followed his homecoming by going into hospital herself.

This was approaching Christmas 1987 - Carole's poignant time of year - and far from problems being over, she was riddled with anxiety for everyone except Paul and herself.

Marc, wading painfully through Basic Training in the army, was suffering from homesickness and unaccustomed military discipline; Victoria appeared to be losing even more weight and seemed unhappier than ever; dad was poorly, recovering very slowly from his surgery, no doubt made worse by mum being ill, while mum, suffering from sickness, stomach pains and swollen legs underwent exploratory tests. Finally, the results of these tests ended with her having a consultation with Dr Khanna and the suggestion of radiotherapy sessions sometime the following year.

Carole was devastated.

So now mum had cancer.

The word was never mentioned, and if mum knew what the problem was, she never discussed it. Nor did dad.

It was a strange Christmas. Just when everything was supposed to be perfect - and in many ways, from just Paul's and Carole's point of view, it was - there was all this. It was hard to find a philosophy that made it all fair and acceptable.

Poor mum and dad. After all they had done for her, and this is what life dealt them back in gratitude. It seemed bitterly unfair. But bitterness wasn't going to help. No doubt there was 'a plan' somewhere, perhaps they had been 'chosen' to learn some special lesson or maybe there was no such thing as fate - just random incidents with the cards temporarily stacked against them. And anyway, a lot of people were much worse off than any of them.

Counting her blessings, Carole felt marginally better again, and as they entered the New Year in 1988, there were indeed a few good events that would be happening shortly.

The first triumph was Marc's Pass Out Parade in March having successfully waded through his six months Basic Training. He was a handsome, healthy and muscle-bound young man with a good future ahead of him and Carole was proud and happy for her son.

The second event for the better was Victoria leaving her boyfriend.

'I've got to move out of the house, mum, it's making me ill,' she cried down the phone.

Her mum had noticed!

But she was so relieved that Victoria now knew it herself. Always a stunningly attractive girl, she was never short of admirers, and towing the line in hot pursuit ready to whisk her away to a safer haven was John.

In fear of violence, Victoria's exit was secretly executed between John, Carole and Victoria one day whilst her boyfriend was out. They must have looked like overt burglars, stealthily creeping in and out of the squalid house laden with goods, even removing the refrigerator and washing machine!

In fact, Victoria seemed to be generally taking stock of herself. She found a pleasant flat in a good area, obtained excellent employment training as a solicitor's clerk and developed a close relationship with John, a caring young man.

No-one ever heard from her undesirable ex-boyfriend again.

Victoria's job prompted Carole to think about herself finding part-time employment. The ever increasing mortgage rate made money tight, especially as they still had so much to do to the cottage. In June, she was due to attend her now annual check-up with Dr Khanna to be followed by mum having radiotherapy. Once those two priorities were over, she would look for work.

Eunice accompanied Carole for the 1988 routine examination - as much an opportune excuse for a good natter as support. With living further away from her now, she saw Eunice less often and it was good to be with her albeit under stressful circumstances. Carole hated these hospital check-ups. Just the smell of the Leicester Royal Infirmary turned her stomach over, flooding her with horrible memories which she knew, now, would never leave her.

Still she remained clear with the next appointment for June 1989. Not until she had stayed free of Hodgkin's Disease for eight years - taking her up to 1991 - would Dr Khanna consider her 'cured'. She didn't feel she would ever have a relapse, but the shadow hovered over her like an unsevered threat. She couldn't imagine life without hospital check-ups!

A more potent reminder came with mum's radiotherapy treatment. Dad was much better now and able to drive the car on good days. But that wasn't every day. Sometimes Carole helped by taking mum for treatment and bringing her home again, which always churned Carole up terribly. On one occasion, Carole's mum stayed in under medical supervision for a couple of days on St Mary's Ward, the same ward where Carole used to receive chemotherapy on Fridays. When Carole went to visit her there, the smell, the familiarity, the memories, were all so unbelievably strong that she thought she would collapse.

Happily, mum began to feel better, and although her cancer was inoperable she perked up under remission with a long term view of better health.

Dad, too, grew increasingly well so Carole decided it was now time to find a job.

Easier said than done.

However, after many applications and rejections, perseverance paid off when she obtained a post in Sales with the Electricity Board. The position offered a new challenge, with opportunities for ongoing training, exams and good promotional prospects. Carole was thrilled if not slightly apprehensive; certainly the nearest she was ever going to get to being a career woman! An early marriage with two young children before she was twenty had meant Carole missed out somewhat on early career prospects. In Africa, circumstance and wealth provided a lifestyle that never demanded her to work, and then, of course, there had been her illness. Consequently, employment now seemed a new and positive challenge.

As Christmas 1988 approached, she went to see her solicitor to finalize divorce proceedings against Nick on the grounds of separation. It was a painful procedure. There always remained some sadness and even affection for him. And him for her. There was no question of the marriage being rekindled however. She was so happy with Paul and Nick and Lynn were planning to marry sometime after the divorce. Maybe it was good that a bit of mutual care had survived if only to vaguely wish the other well. But it didn't help the final curtain.

'Bet you're glad that's over!' joked an ill-humoured solicitor insensitively as Carole's shaking hand swore on oath the official death of love.

On the whole, Christmas and the New Year were actually the happiest and most trouble free for a long time. Indeed, the whole of 1989 remained free of problems! Both Carole's parents and the children were settled in their various roles and all enjoying the best of health circumstance would allow.

She and Paul were so happy in Windrush Cottage, it now boasting a brand new thatch, a fully modernized kitchen and being prettily decorated throughout.

At seven years old, Pinky enjoyed boisterous good health in her country surroundings. Middle-age had slowed her down a little, but she could still run a good mile given half a chance! Thumper had grown into a roguish, rural tom, able to outwit all but the smartest of prey and often returned home with his latest catch in the misguided hope of approval.

Carole's work with the Electricity Board proved rewarding, providing her with the stimulus of study in sales in addition to a little extra cash and cheerful company. Victoria, too, had decided to further her education, working hard at evening classes for 'A' level Physics and Law. This was the groundwork of training towards her eventual ambition of obtaining a Law degree and becoming a Legal Secretary.

Victoria had amazed them all. From a totally rebellious, obnoxious adolescent she had become this intelligent, capable, caring and responsible young lady. Now sharing a home with John, Carole once again found the lovely daughter and friend she thought she'd lost for ever.

It was Paul, this time, who wanted a change of career and he left the RAF after twelve years of service to work as a Project Engineer with a thriving new engineering company.

Carole's June 1989 annual check-up with Dr Khanna gave her another twelve month reprieve, and the only flaw in the entire year was finding out Nick had married Lynn without even telling Carole or his own children.

It was more than a year later, in January 1991, when something happened to make her reflect deeply on all the trials and tribulations of the last decade. And that was when her friend, Marianne, phoned suggesting they write her story.

The previous June had seen Carole through her annual check-up with Dr Khanna without any problems, and, all being well, the next routine examination due June 18th 1991 would be the last.

Carole would then be considered cured of Hodgkin's Disease.

Marianne was enthusiastic, believing the whole saga of her broken marriage and cancer to be an inspirational story of triumph. It sounded exciting, though Carole claimed modest possession of courage, having really had little alternative.

'But that's just it!' Marianne insisted. 'It's the fact that you are a normal human being with fears and weaknesses that makes it all so important. You're not famous or rich, you've had no special privileges or perks or treatment - you could be anyone. You're just Carole!'

CHAPTER TWENTY-FIVE

The End Begins

With that, Carole invited Marianne to come round one day the following week to discuss things further.

Marianne had previously had short stories and articles published in magazines but never anything as ambitious as a book, so the whole idea presented an enormous challenge to both of them. Paul was intrigued by the thought of writing a biography but held realistic reservations.

'Do you both realize how much work would have to go into it? And then, after 50,000 words, and a few years of hard slog, the struggle would then be to find a publisher.'

He was right, they both knew.

But there was something else in the project that was probably more important than anyone else could understand. And that was the opportunity for Carole to express the pain, spill out the tears, discard the anguish, the anger, the bottled-up bitterness. She still carried a lot of old luggage within her that could only be thrown away by rummaging through it and having a good clear out. She faced a lot of disturbing memories by unearthing the past, but maybe, as the story unfolded bringing health and happiness, she would be able to celebrate yet again - and this time, totally free of the past.

A kind of therapy.

'Of course, we will need permission from Dr Silverstein in Nairobi and Dr Khanna if we use their real names - and from anyone else, for that matter,' said Marianne, perched uncomfortably on the edge of the seat to allow Thumper full regal reclining rights to his armchair.

Pinky glanced up at Marianne, hoping for her biscuit rather than inclusion in her book.

'Yes, Pinky,' continued Marianne, misinterpreting the dog's sudden interest, 'you'll be in it, too.'

The first 'book session' left them both drained and with only enough material for one chapter. And all the time, they were tempting fate with the premature message of receiving absolution from Hodgkin's Disease - not due, if at all, until June.

Their first big thrill was an encouraging letter from Dr David Silverstein of the Kenyatta National Hospital in Nairobi giving them permission to reveal his identity and wishing them the best of luck. Friends and relatives supported the project and nearly all of them were happy to reveal their own names. Then they received copyright permission from the publishers John Wiley and Sons to draw on any medical reference from the book *All About Cancer* by Chris Williams. And eventually, about six chapters into the book, they wrote to Dr Khanna.

It was ages before they received a reply, and when they did, it was a short, direct letter asking to see the rough draft so far before allowing permission to use either his name or that of the Leicester Royal Infirmary.

'Oh dear,' Carole whined to Marianne, 'I bet he won't like what we've put about him.'

'Well, it's all true...' protested Marianne, equally unsure.

A copy of the manuscript was duly left with Dr Khanna's secretary, leaving them to await his verdict. Meanwhile, another welcome response had come from the Hodgkin's Disease and Lymphoma Association (their address and phone number are in the Appendix at the end of this book) who offered them their full support and encouragement. Carole had only just learned about their existence; it would have been a very great comfort to have had their care and concern in the past - but at least this gave her an opportunity to advertise their presence for any other Hodgkin's Disease sufferers.

Carole's annual appointment with Dr Khanna drew near. He had had the manuscript for five weeks and they had heard nothing. Marianne was frantic to get it back, and both of them felt embarrassed that they had wasted his time, burdening him with a futile pie-eyed fantasy of writing a book. Persistent phone calls to his secretary came to nothing. He was either busy, in America, or would be given the message - all of which merely served to protect him from their irritating interference.

Finally, Marianne wrote him a brief letter reminding him of Carole's appointment and suggested they collect the rough draft at that time. In truth, they doubted he would remember what they were on about and feared the copy was long since lost.

But for Carole, the over-riding factor of her June 18th appointment was the possibility of it being the last. She was always anxious before seeing Dr Khanna. This time, she was terrified. Would he associate her with the person in the manuscript he had? Did he remember he had a manuscript? Did he remember *her?*

Marianne came too for this appointment. She also used the opportunity to get a feel for the place, the infirmary, the waiting area, and to chat with other patients. They even took themselves down to the 'Megavolt Suite', meandering along corridors, Carole pointing out some toilets where she'd once been sick following chemotherapy, then back via the closed doors of St Mary's Ward and the private annex she'd been rushed to after her close brush with death.

It was all still there. Nothing ever changed. The doors, the walls, the smells... It still felt just like yesterday.

'Hey, we'd better get back to the Waiting Room!' Carole suddenly exclaimed, looking at her watch. 'It's almost time for my appointment.'

Nervously, they both headed back and joined all the others who were also waiting to see the doctor.

'There's Dr Khanna!' Carole whispered urgently to Marianne, as he breezed in and out of the consulting room.

'That's just what I thought he'd look like!' murmured Marianne.

Suddenly, Dr Khanna's dark eyes caught Carole's.

'Ah. I want to see you, don't I,' he said as a statement of fact rather than a question. Then, with white coat blowing open, he rushed away. Marianne and Carole looked at each other.

'He remembers!' they chorused.

Shortly after, a nurse came up to her.

'Dr Khanna is not receiving appointments here this afternoon. However, he has told me you are to see him and must go down to where he is, in the radiotherapy department.'

Marianne was pleased. Now she was about to see the Megavolt Suite from the inside.

The oppressive heat and claustrophobic depth of the radiotherapy department filled Carole with memories as she recalled her fourteenth wedding anniversary which had coincided with that very first treatment so many years ago.

After a lengthy wait, Dr Khanna called for her.

'Best of luck,' winked Marianne.

Carole couldn't believe it!

Not only had Dr Khanna remembered the manuscript, he apologized for the delay in it's return saying he had wanted to see her in person for permission to photocopy it! Moreover, he happily gave permission to reveal his identity and that of the Leicester Royal Infirmary. In addition to *that*, he volunteered a duplicate copy of all her medical notes covering the complete episode of Hodgkin's Disease from the original biopsy in Nairobi to the present day.

And there was more to come!

The examination revealed no problem, followed by a blood test that was fine and a chest X-ray which proved clear.

In effect, Carole was now considered cured.

She had served her time and with a warm smile, a twinkle in his eye and the compassion of a doctor who has achieved the ultimate success, Dr Khanna told her there was no need to make any further appointment.

Clutching both the manuscript copy and medical notes, Marianne and Carole headed towards the car in the Infirmary car park. Carole's mind was a whirl. For eight years she had dreamed of being free from cancer - and now she was. Where was the fanfare of trumpets? The flying flags? But in her heart, a thousand screams were cheering euphorically: 'I'm free! I'm cured! I'm cured!'

It was unreal; she couldn't believe it.

'Thank God for that!' laughed Marianne. 'Now we can carry on with the story!'

Carole passed all the paperwork over to Marianne and started to manoeuvre the car out onto the road. Dr Khanna's final words still echoed in her mind, and thoughts raced around in dizzy relief. Marianne was chattering away, flipping through the medical notes with enthusiastic energy, but she hardly heard a word until her voice suddenly changed tone.

Puzzled, Carole turned to face her and saw Marianne's hand up to her mouth. Their eyes met. She looked shocked.

'Did you know you were stage III Hodgkin's Disease?'

'No,' Carole admitted quietly.

She dropped Marianne off at her home and carried on first to see mum and dad.

Their own health now was fairly stable, mum was still in remission and dad was now much better than he'd been for a long time. When she told them the great news, they were both absolutely thrilled and delighted that she could at last put it all behind her.

Next, she drove back home to Windrush Cottage. A strange sense of purpose mingled with euphoria, almost as if everything had been part of a plan - worthwhile. It seemed important to use this energy, but as yet, she didn't know how or on what. Perhaps the book would be important. Others had to know that if she could survive Hodgkin's Disease, anyone could. And not only that, but through the fight, or the struggles, a supreme God given strength could be found that was so reassuring as to make no problem insurmountable.

But what was she saying?!

As soon as she put the key in the door, Carole burst into tears.

'Pinky!' she wailed, 'I'm cured, I'm cured, I'm cured!'

Pinky wagged her little tail excitedly, thrilled as always to see her but not quite sure whether Carole was happy or sad.

Then she phoned Eunice, followed by Victoria - both expressed total happiness for her and shared her complete feelings of triumph and euphoria.

After that, she wrote to Marc who was stationed at Soest in Germany, then scribbled a brief note to Nick who'd asked to be told how she'd got on.

Last but not least was Paul. Unfortunately, it had to be this day when he was away on business, but he had promised to ring home as soon as he could.

At seven o'clock he phoned - and actually forgot to ask about Carole's hospital appointment until she gently reminded him!

'Oh, sorry! Of course, I always knew you were fine, it never occurred to me otherwise - but honestly, I am pleased. Really pleased.'

After she put the receiver down, she felt a bit flat. Everyone was really happy for her - but at the end of the day, only she herself really understood how much she'd been through and how much today had meant. And now she was going to spend the evening alone.

But perhaps that was strangely significant. Although she desperately wanted to be able to share what was really going on inside her, she also wanted to be alone. Ultimately, it had been a solitary journey. Without friendship, family, love and support, she would have been emotionally crippled, not to mention the practical mess, she knew. But the heartache, the soul searching, the final quest for strength - and the resultant independence, she'd done alone. For a moment, she reflected back to the woman she had been when the cancer had first been diagnosed; she'd still been a child, unable to make her own decisions, let alone act upon them. Poor me, she thought, feeling momentarily more sorry for the girl who hadn't suffered, than the woman who had! She wondered what would have happened if she'd never had Hodgkin's Disease. Would she have stayed with Nick? Put up with everything because she wouldn't have had the courage to do otherwise?

Of course, she could have died. But death no longer held as much fear for Carole as being sick. A multitude of ambivalent thoughts tossed around her mind. Maybe she still didn't know anything?

Ah, but one thing she did know… she wanted a drink!!

Carole went to the wine rack in the kitchen, opened a bottle of dry, white wine and poured out a glass for herself.

Both Pinky and Thumper looked up at her expectantly. The kitchen was always a source of optimism for them.

'Oh, well, you understand, don't you Pinky? You've had a bit of a rough ride, too,' Carole smiled and gently stroked her head. 'But I'll tell you this, old girl, we made it!'

135

Postscript

Carole continues to enjoy excellent health, living life to the full and looking radiantly well. She celebrated her third wedding anniversary to Paul in February 1996 and they both still live happily in Windrush Cottage.

Victoria holds a successful position in law, and is contentedly settled in a long term relationship. Marc has spent time travelling but is now living in the Midlands with good career prospects ahead of him. Both of them maintain a close and loving bond with their mother.

Sadly, Carole's mother finally succumbed to bowel cancer and eventually lost her fight; her father still lives in Enderby in the same cosy, two bedroomed terraced house.

Pinky died of old age in Carole's arms some time ago but the memory of Pinky will live forever. Thumper regrettably lost his life in a road accident in the village. They still have two cats and a golden retriever, now two, called Honey.

Carole's energy and vitality is as good as, if not better than, most. She suffers no weakness as a result of having had Hodgkin's Disease with the subsequent treatment and can hope and expect to live a long and healthy life.

Appendix

Useful addresses

Hodgkin's Disease and Lymphoma Association
PO Box 275
Haddenham
Aylesbury
Bucks
HP17 8JJ
Telephone helpline: 01844 291500

The Association is a national charity formed in 1986 to help the six thousand new cases of Lymphoma (cancers of the lymph glands), which occur in Britain each year. It offers emotional support and information to patients, their families and carers, and covers both Hodgkin's disease and the non Hodgkin's lymphomas. Enquirers may be linked with helpers who have experience of the disease and local groups are being formed in a steady programme designed to meet patients' needs. Cancer related books, tapes and videos are available on loan, and the Association produces a quarterly newsletter issued free to enquirers and members.

BACUP (British Association of Cancer United Patients)
3, Bath Place
Rivington Street
London
EC2A 3JR
Tel: Administration 0171 696 9003 Fax: 0171 696 9002
Cancer Information Service Freephone: 0800 18 11 99
Cancer Counselling Service (London): 0171 696 9000
(Glasgow): 0141 553 1553

BACUP provides free information and support for people affected by cancer through an information service, a counselling service and publications on many different types of cancer, treatments and ways of living with cancer.

CancerLink

17 Britannia Street
London
WC1X 9JN
Tel: 0171 833 2451

9 Castle Terrace
Edinburgh
EH1 2DP
Tel: 0131 228 5557

CancerLink provide free, confidential support and information about cancer to everyone, nationwide.

Cancer Relief MacMillan Fund
Anchor House
15-19 Britten Street
London
SW3 3TZ
Tel: 0171 351 7811

The Cancer Relief MacMillan Fund supports and develops services to provide skilled care, including MacMillan nurses, and provides financial assistance through grants.

The Leukaemia Care Society
14, Kingfisher Court,
Venny Bridge
Pinhoe
Exeter
Devon
EX4 8JN
Tel: 01392 464848

The society offers support, low or no cost caravan holidays and financial assistance in times of difficulty to those with Hodgkin's Disease and Non Hodgkin's Lymphoma as well as leukaemia and allied blood disorders.

Marie Curie Cancer Care
28 Belgrave Square
London
SW1X 8QG
Tel: 0171 235 3325

This provides specialist nursing care for cancer patients through its eleven Hospice centres, spread throughout the United Kingdom. There are also 6000 Marie Curie nurses who provide free, practical nursing care at home, 24 hours a day. The Cancer Research Institute has been set up for the education of health care professionals.